SRA

LANGUAGE ACTIVITY MASTERS

SRA McGraw-Hill

Columbus, Ohio

A Division of The **McGraw·Hill** Companies

Acknowledgement

The publisher would like to thank Therese Snyder of
Westlake Village, California for her help in preparing this Activity
Masters book.

SRA/McGraw-Hill

A Division of The McGraw·Hill Companies

Copyright © 2001 by SRA/McGraw-Hill.

Send all inquiries to:
SRA/McGraw-Hill
8787 Orion Place
Columbus, OH 43240-4027

Printed in the United States of America.

ISBN 0-02-684499-0

4 5 6 7 8 9 MAZ 05 04 03

Table of Contents

Activities

Newsletters

Introduction

This book consists of 30 activity lessons with accompanying blackline masters. These activity masters correlate with the lessons in *Language for Learning* and *Español to English*. The activities reinforce the skills and concepts taught in these programs.

This book also contains reproducible newsletters that can be sent home at regular intervals to the families of the children in your class. These newsletters give information about what the children are learning in their daily language lessons. The newsletters also give families ideas about additional activities that they can do at home to complement the activities that are being done in the classroom.

Time Requirements

One activity is scheduled after every fifth lesson, starting with lesson 5. Activities should not be scheduled as part of the regular language lesson. The activities are a treat for the children and should be considered a bonus for daily work "well done."

Materials

In addition to the blackline masters, children will need specific materials for the activities. Each lesson contains a "Materials Needed for Lesson" box that lists the materials needed for that particular lesson. The major supplies that you will need for these lessons are crayons, scissors, glue, hole puncher, and tape.

Preparation

Before presenting each activity, read through the directions. Be sure to have all materials assembled and the blackline masters copied. It's a good idea to complete the activity yourself before presenting it to the children.

Object Concentration Game
Object Identification

Materials Needed for Lesson
For each child you will need 1 copy of BLM 5, crayons, and scissors.

Presenting the Activity

1. (Make copies of the blackline master.)

2. (Show the children a copy of BLM 5.) **See if you can tell me the names of all the things on this page. Watch for my signal. When I touch something, tell me the name.**

   • (Point to the tree.) **What is this?** (Touch.) *A tree.*
   Yes, a tree.
   • (Point to the shoe.) **What is this?** (Touch.) *A shoe.*
   Yes, a shoe.
   • (Continue until children have identified all the pictures.)

3. (Give each child a copy of BLM 5 and crayons. Have the children color the pictures.)

4. (Give each child scissors. Show them how to cut the pictures apart by following the dotted lines. Help children as necessary.)

5. **Today we are going to play a concentration game with some cards. Concentration means that you need to think about and remember what you have seen.**

6. (To begin the game, lay one set of cards face down on the table. The first player draws two cards. If the cards match, the player identifies the item in the pictures, keeps the cards, and takes another turn. If the items don't match, the player turns the cards back over, and another player takes a turn. The children will soon discover that if they can remember where certain cards are, they will be able to match them more quickly. The game continues until all the cards are matched.)

7. (Once players become good at playing the game, they can play with a partner.)

8. (Children can take the cards home and play the game with family members.)

Roll the Cube! Actions Block
Actions

Materials Needed for Lesson
For each child you will need 1 copy of BLM 10, scissors, and glue.

Presenting the Activity

1. (Make copies of the blackline master. Make one Actions Cube to use for an example.)

2. Get ready to do some actions. Watch my hand. Remember to wait for the signal.

   • Everybody, stand up. (Signal. Children stand up.)
   • Everybody, sit down. (Signal. Children sit down.)
   • Everybody, touch your nose. (Signal. Children touch their nose.)
   • Everybody, touch your head. (Signal. Children touch their head.)
   • Everybody, touch your ear. (Signal. Children touch their ear.)
   • Everybody, touch your arm. (Signal. Children touch their arm.)

3. Let's do those actions again. (Repeat step 2.)

4. Today we're going to make a game we can play with actions. (Show the children a copy of BLM 10.) See if you can do the actions these pictures show. Watch for my signal. When I touch something, you do the action. (Touch each action picture and check children's response.)

5. (Give each child a copy of BLM 10 and crayons. Direct children to color the pictures.)

6. (Show the children the cube you have made. Give each child a pair of scissors. Show them how to cut out the cube and fold it on the fold lines. Help children as necessary. Help children put glue on the tabs and fold the cube together.)

7. (Use the cube you have made to play a game with the group. The first player rolls the cube. Everyone performs the action that falls with the face up. A second player then rolls the cube. After the group becomes good at playing the game, they can play it with partners. The children can take the cubes home and play the game with family members.)

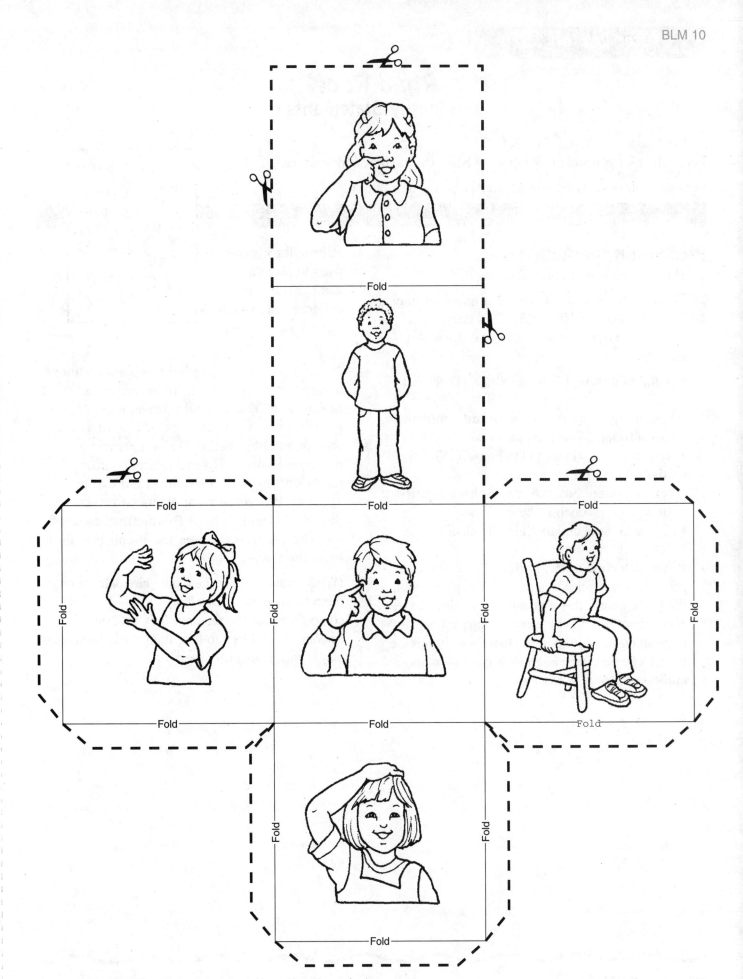

Fold

Fold

Fold — Fold

Fold

Fold

Fold — Fold

Fold

Fold — Fold

Fold

Fold

Road Race!
Identity Statements

Materials Needed for Lesson

For each child you will need 1 copy of BLM 15, crayons, and scissors.

For each pair of children you will need a penny or a button.

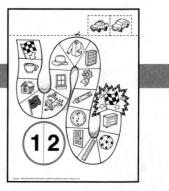

Presenting the Activity

1. (Make copies of the blackline master.)

2. Today we are going to make a game to play. (Hold up a copy of BLM 15.) This game has pictures. Let's see how many of these you know.

   • (Point to the cup.) What is this? (Touch.) *A cup.*
     Yes, a cup. Say the whole thing about the cup. (Touch.) *This is a cup.*
   • Next picture. (Point to the house.) What is this? (Touch.) *A house.*
     Yes, a house. Say the whole thing about the house. (Touch.) *This is a house.*
   • (Continue until children identify all of the pictures.)

3. (Give each child a copy of BLM 15, crayons, and scissors. Direct children to color the pictures on the game board, the cars, and the tossing circle. Show them how to cut away the top part of the page along the dotted line. Then they cut out the cars. *Note: Cars may be glued to cardboard to make them easier to handle.*)

4. (Divide the class into pairs to play the game. Each pair of children will use one game board and one set of cars.)

   Now we are ready to play the game. Choose a car. Put your car on the arrow at the start of the race. You will take turns tossing your penny (button) on the circle. If your penny (button) lands on the "1," your car can move one space. If your penny (button) lands on the "2," your car can move two spaces. When your car stops you must "Say the whole thing" about the picture it lands on. The car that crosses the finish line first wins the game.

5. (While children play the game, circulate among them to make sure they "Say the whole thing" correctly about the pictures they land on. Encourage children to take their game home and play it with family members.)

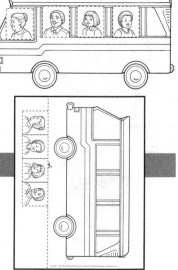

The People on the Bus
Identity Statements

Materials Needed for Lesson

For each child you will need 1 copy of BLM 20, crayons, scissors, and glue.

Presenting the Activity

1. (Make copies of the blackline master.)

2. (Show children a copy of BLM 20.) **When I touch something, you tell me about it.**

   - (Point to the bus.) **Everybody, what is this?** (Touch.) *A bus.*
     Say the whole thing. (Touch.) *This is a bus.*
   - (Point to the girl.) **Everybody, what is this?** (Touch.) *A girl.*
     Say the whole thing. (Touch.) *This is a girl.*
   - (Point to the boy.) **Everybody, what is this?** (Touch.) *A boy.*
     Say the whole thing. (Touch.) *This is a boy.*
   - (Point to the man.) **Everybody, what is this?** (Touch.) *A man.*
     Say the whole thing. (Touch.) *This is a man.*
   - (Point to the woman.) **Everybody, what is this?** (Touch.) *A woman.*
     Say the whole thing. (Touch.) *This is a woman.*

3. **Let's do that again.** (Repeat step 2.)

4. (Give each child a copy of BLM 20 and crayons. Direct the children to color the bus and the people.)

5. (Give each child scissors and glue. Show the children how to cut off the pictures of the people along the dotted line. They can then cut the pictures apart and glue them in the bus windows. Help children as necessary.)

6. (Allow the children to take turns pointing to the bus and the people on the bus. Children should "Say the whole thing." For example, a child might say, *This is a girl.*)

7. (Sing "The Wheels on the Bus.")

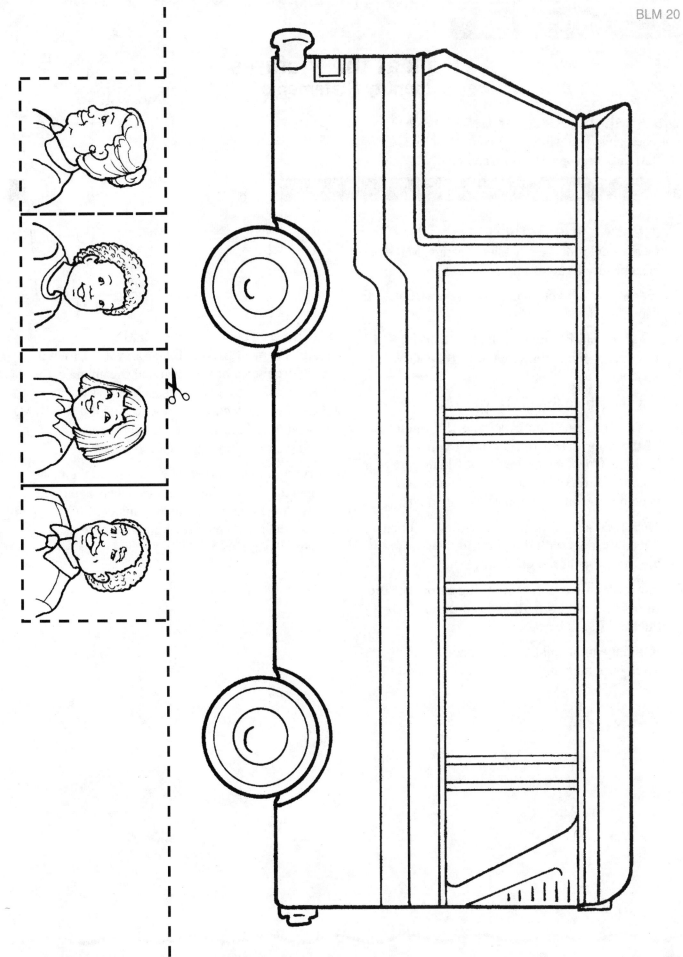

Peek at the Pictures
Identity Statements

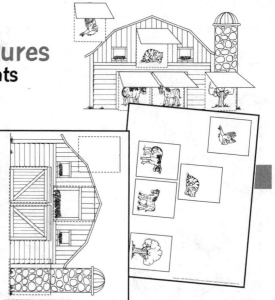

Materials Needed for Lesson

For each child you will need 1 copy of BLM 25A, 1 copy of BLM 25B, crayons, scissors, and glue.

Presenting the Activity

1. (Make copies of the blackline masters. Make one barn picture as an example. See step 6.)

2. (Show children your completed barn picture with flaps closed.)

   Look at this picture. (Point to the barn.) **This is a barn. Everybody, what is this?** (Touch.) *A barn.*

   Say the whole thing. (Touch.) *This is a barn.*

3. **Let's see what lives in a barn. I'll open one of the doors. You tell me what you see inside.** (Open one of the doors. Children say for example, *A cat.* Continue until all doors have been opened and all animals identified.)

4. **Now let's see what lives outside the barn.** (Open the door with the bird and the door with the tree for children to identify.)

5. **Now, when I touch something in one of the doors, you will say the whole thing.** (Touch the cat.) *This is a cat.*

   (Continue until children have made a statement about each animal.)

6. (Give each child a copy of BLM 25A and a copy of BLM 25B and crayons. Direct the children to color the barn and the animals. Cut along the dotted lines on each child's barn picture. Show children how to glue the two BLMs together. Make sure that no glue is applied over the pictures under the doors.)

7. (After glue has dried, have children take turns opening the windows on their barns and making a statement about the animal inside. Children can take their barn pictures home to share with family members.)

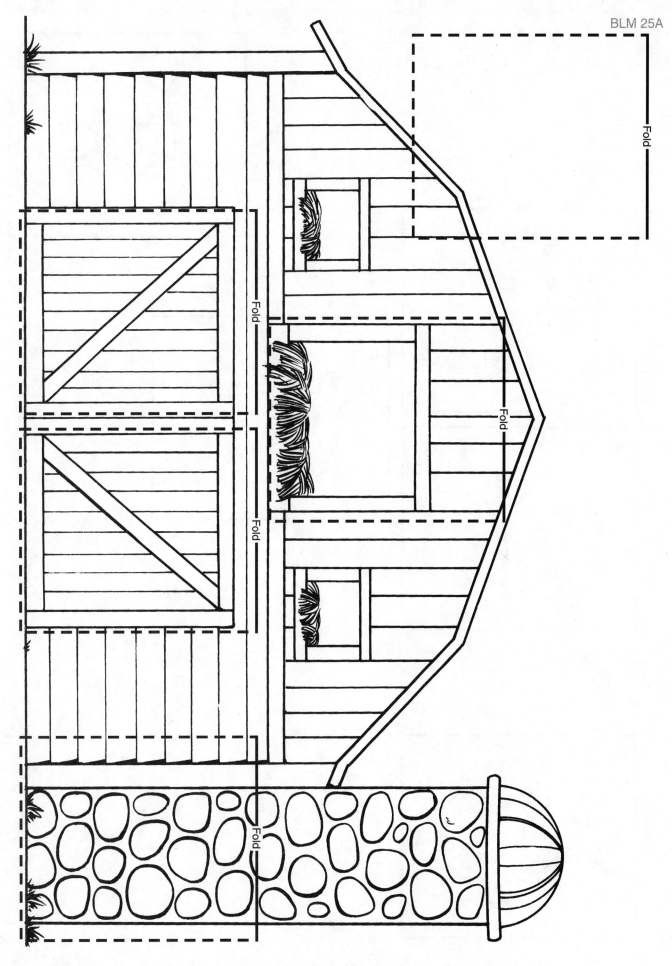

Fold

Fold

Fold

Fold

Fold

Fold

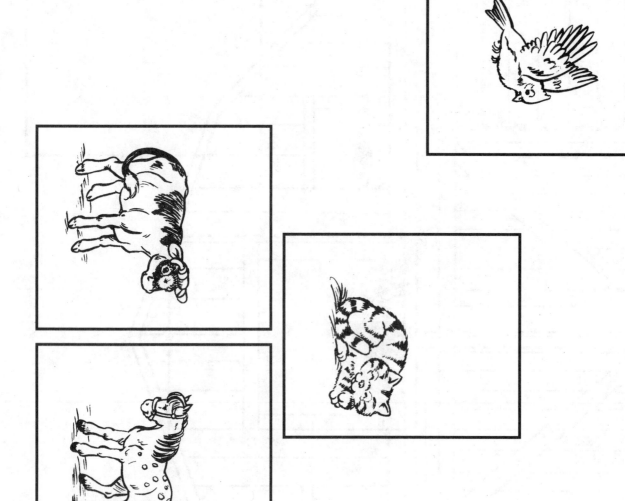

Whose Shoe?
Common Information

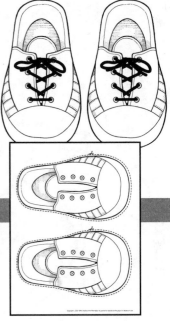

Materials Needed for Lesson

For each child you will need 1 copy of BLM 30, crayons, scissors, glue, 1 sheet of construction paper, and 2 twelve-inch pieces of yarn in assorted colors.

Hole puncher

Presenting the Activity

1. (Make copies of the blackline master.)

2. Today you are going to make a pair of shoes and play a game with them. You can make your shoes any color you want. Then I'll give you some pretty yarn to use for the laces. (Give each child a copy of BLM 30 and crayons. Direct the children to color their shoes. Remind them that a pair of shoes should match, so they should color both shoes the same color.)

3. (Give each child scissors, glue, and a piece of construction paper. Direct the children to glue the picture of shoes to the construction paper. Then they can cut out the shoes.)

4. (Punch holes in the shoes for the laces. Let each child choose a color of yarn for his or her shoelaces. Remind the children that the laces should match. Both shoes should have the same color laces. Help the children as necessary to lace the shoes.)

5. Now we will play the game. Everybody, put one of your shoes in a pile on the table. Hold your other shoe in your hands. (Select one child to choose a shoe from the pile. That child asks, "Whose shoe?" The group responds by saying the name of the owner. For example, the group might say, "John's shoe." If it is not John's shoe, he can say, "No, that is not my shoe," and the group gets another guess. If the shoe is John's shoe, he can say, "Yes, that is my shoe." You give the shoe to its owner. Continue playing until all shoes have been returned to their owners.)

6. (Another game you can play is "Musical Shoes." Children sit in a circle. While music plays, they pass the shoes around the circle. When you stop the music, the children take turns guessing whose shoes they are holding.)

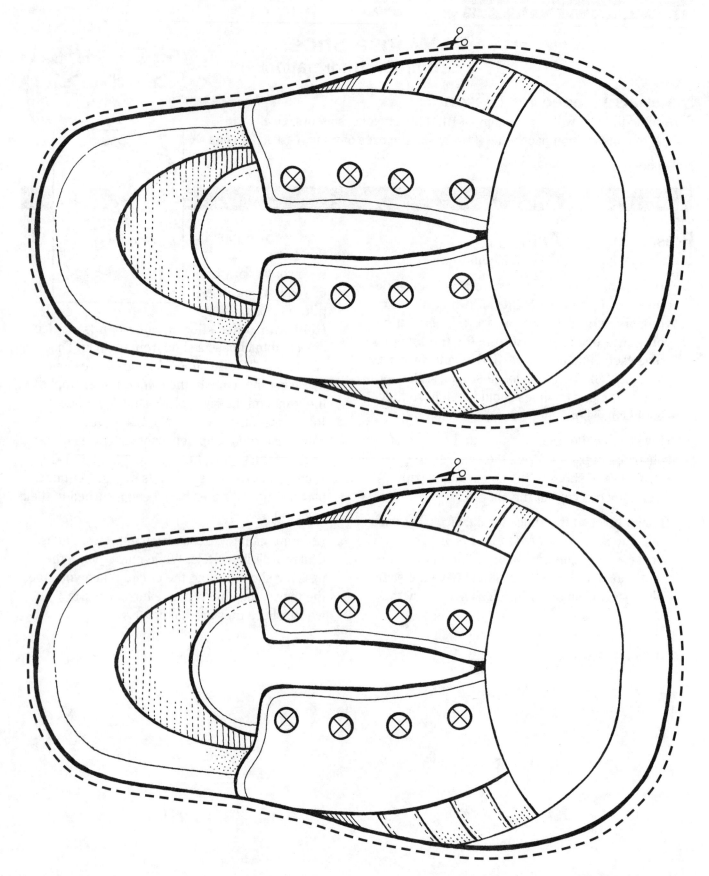

Spin a Person
Parts of the Body

Materials Needed for Lesson

For each child you will need 1 copy of BLM 35B, 4 brads, crayons, and scissors.
For each group of children you will need 1 copy of BLM 35A and 1 brad.

Hole puncher

Glue

Cardboard

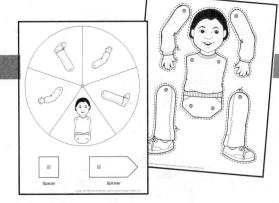

Presenting the Activity

1. (Make copies of blackline masters.)

2. (Glue the copy of blackline master 35A to cardboard. Cut out the spinner, dial, and spacer. You may wish to have a child color the spinner before assembling it.)

3. (Give each child a copy of BLM 35B and crayons. Direct the children to color the body parts and cut them out. Help the children as needed. Punch the holes as indicated on the pattern. Have each child place his or her pile of body parts on the table.)

4. **Today we are going to play a game. We'll spin the spinner and see if we remember the names of these body parts. I'll go first.**

5. (Spin the spinner and name the body part. Pass the spinner to a child. That child spins and, if he or she successfully names the body part, takes it from the pile. If the spinner lands on a part the child already has, the child spins again. The spinner keeps passing until each child has enough pieces to assemble parts.)

6. (Give each child four brads. Help them as necessary in assembling their bodies. Ask them to take turns naming the body parts of their completed body.)

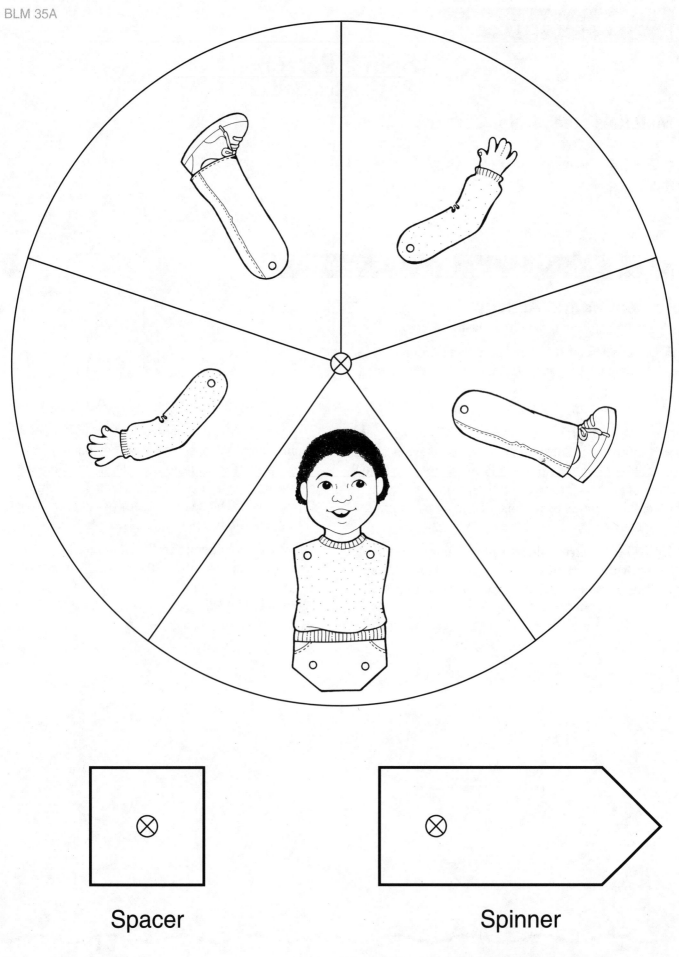

Spacer

Spinner

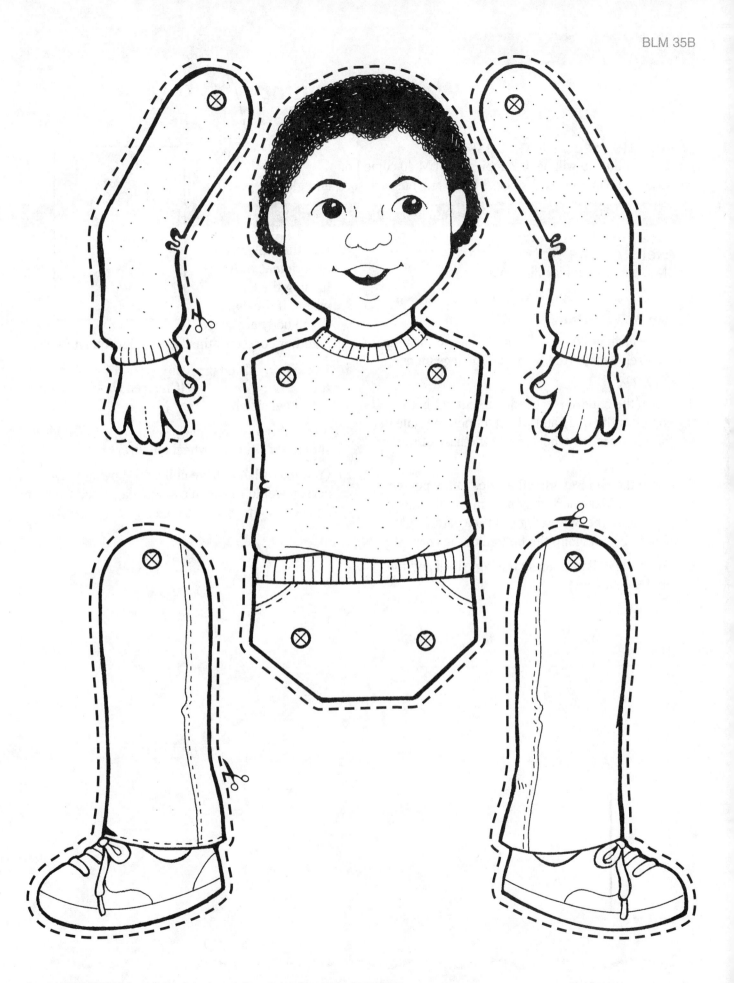

Walking/Running
Actions

Materials Needed for Lesson

For each child you will need 2 copies of BLM 40 copied on construction paper or card stock, 1 brad, crayons, scissors, and glue.

Presenting the Activity

1. (Make copies of blackline masters.)

2. Today we are going to make a person who can walk or run.

3. (Give each child two copies of BLM 40. Ask the children to color the body and the legs on one copy only.)

4. (Help the children as needed to cut out both copies of the body and wheel. Punch the hole in the center of the wheel and at the base of the body.)

5. (Help the children glue the sides of the person together. Make sure they put only a thin line of glue along the outer edges of the coat. No glue should be put along the bottom of the coat.)

6. (Help the children insert the leg wheel and the brad. See above.)

7. (Let the children experiment with turning the leg wheel. If the copies of the body are glued together correctly, the leg wheel will turn freely.)

8. Everybody, hold up your person. Show me how a person walks. (Children should turn the leg wheel slowly.)

9. Now, show me how a person runs. (Children should turn the leg wheel quickly.)

10. (You may wish to have children show how the person would move on a sunny day, a rainy day, a snowy day, an icy day, a cold day, a hot day.)

Build an Elephant
Part/Whole

Materials Needed for Lesson

For each child you will need 1 copy of BLM 45B copied on gray construction paper, 1 piece of 8 ½" x 11" cardboard, scissors, glue, and 1 marker (buttons of assorted colors).

For each group of children you will need 1 copy of BLM 45A and 1 number cube.

Presenting the Activity

1. (Glue the copy of BLM 45A to a piece of 8 ½" x 11" cardboard. You may want to ask a child to color the game board.)

2. (Cut each copy of BLM 45B into squares to create sets of elephant body parts.)

3. **Today we are going play a game to make an elephant.** (Give each child a different color button.)

   Put a marker on the start arrow. (Each child and the teacher should place a different color button on the start arrow.)

4. **Listen. You will roll the number cube. You will move your marker as many spaces as the number cube shows. When you land on an elephant body part, you can take it from the pile. Then you must say the whole thing about that body part. If you land on a part you already have, you have to wait for another turn.**

5. **My turn.** (You roll the number cube and move the marker the correct number of spaces. You take the correct body part from the pile and "Say the whole thing." Example: "An elephant has legs." Give the number cube to a child.)

6. (The game continues until all children have enough parts to create an elephant. It may take two trips around the game board for each child to get all the parts. *Note: When a child lands on "legs," the child can take two legs.*)

7. (Allow children to cut out the elephant parts and glue them to the body.)

8. (Ask the children to take turns naming the elephant body parts with their completed elephants.)

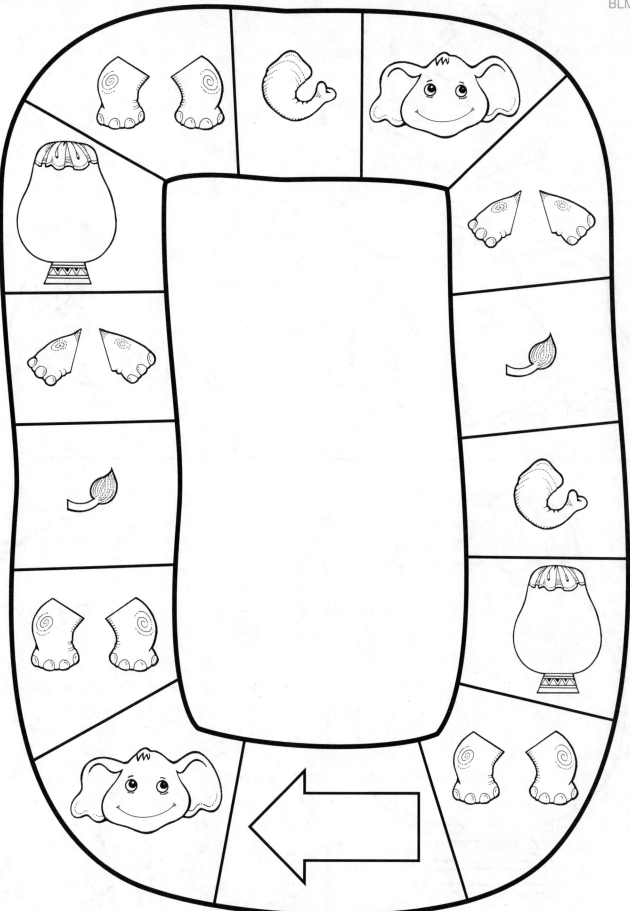

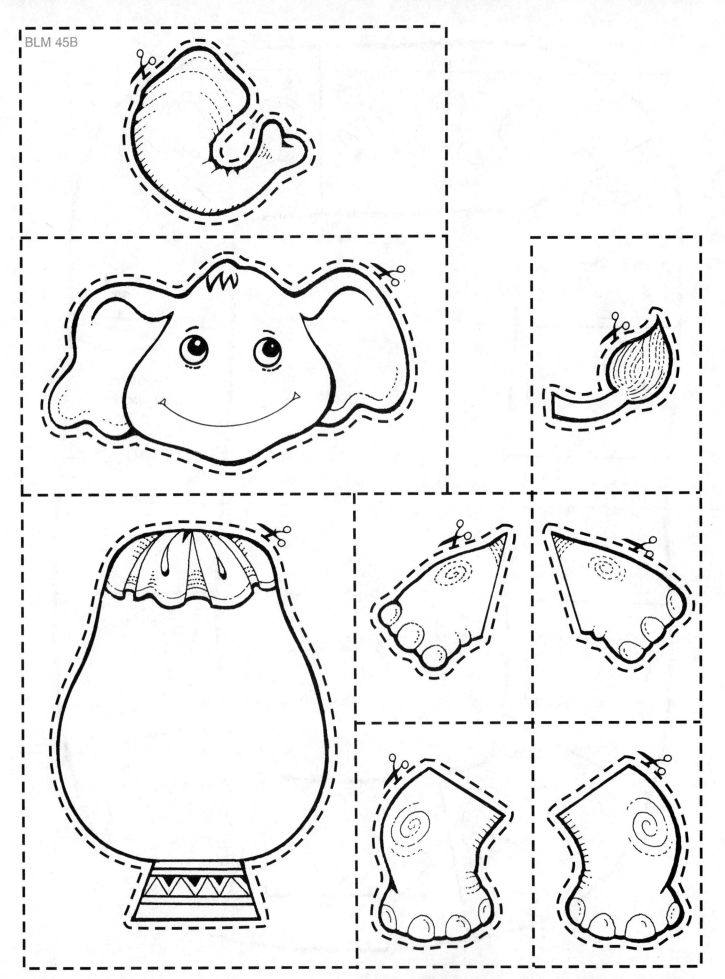

BLM 45B

Bear Hat
Vocabulary

Materials Needed for Lesson

For each child you will need 1 copy of BLM 50 copied on brown construction paper, scissors, and 1 twelve-inch piece of yarn.

Hole puncher

Presenting the Activity

1. (Make copies of the blackline master.)

2. Today we are going to make something you wear on your head. What do you call something you wear on your head? (Signal.) *A hat.*

   Yes, a hat.

3. This is a special kind of hat that looks like a bear's face. (Give each child a copy of BLM 50 and a pair of scissors.) Cut out your bear hat. Follow the dotted lines. (Help children as necessary.)

4. (After children have cut out their bear hats, punch the holes in the sides and help them tie the ends together with yarn. Children can put on their hats.)

5. What are you wearing on your head? (Signal.) *A hat.*

6. What animal does your hat look like? (Signal.) *A bear.*

7. (You may wish to read the children a book about bears such as *Goldilocks and the Three Bears* by Jan Brett, *Winnie the Pooh* by A. A. Milne, or *Can't You Sleep, Little Bear?* by Martin Waddell. The children may act out one of the stories using their bear hats.)

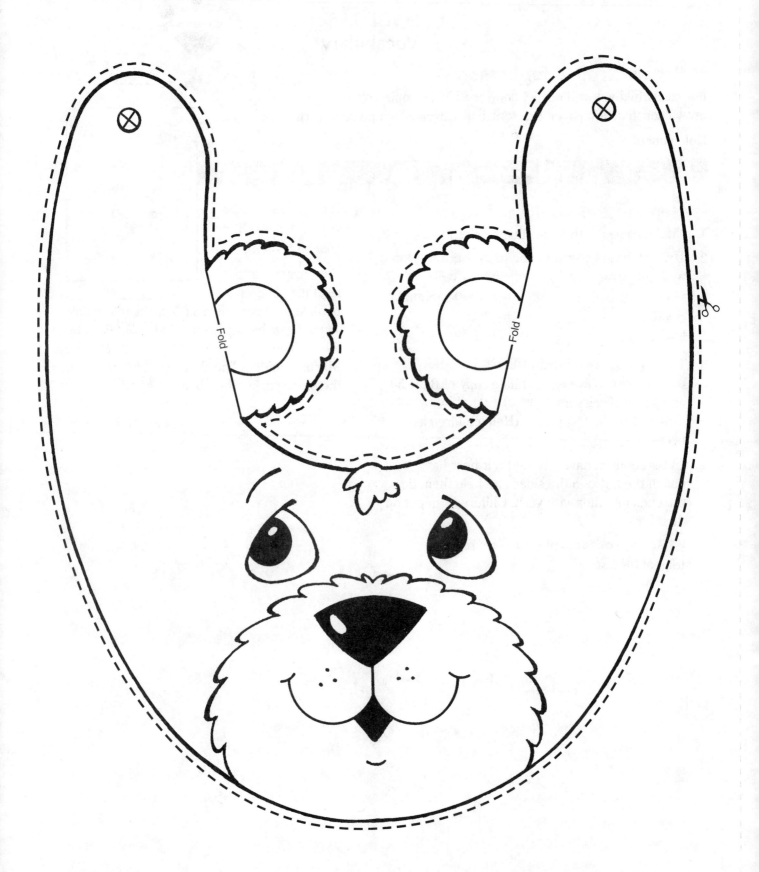

Fold

Fold

Short to Long Doggie
Opposites
Short/Long

Materials Needed for Lesson

For each child you will need 1 copy of BLM 55, 2 craft sticks, crayons, scissors, glue, 1 drinking straw or chenille wire, and tape.

Hole puncher

Presenting the Activity

1. (Make copies of the blackline master.)

2. Today we are going to make something that can be short or long.

3. (Give each child a copy of BLM 55.)

4. (Ask the children to color the parts of the dog's body. Direct them to cut off the bottom part of the page along the dotted line. Then they can cut out the parts of the dog's body along the dotted lines. Help children as needed.)

5. (Show the children how to fold the bottom part of the page along the fold lines to create a pleated/fan effect. Help children as needed.)

6. (Punch a hole in the center of the bunch of folds. Children can then push a straw or chenille wire through the hole. Tape the straw or wire to the back of the dog's head.)

7. (Help the children glue the edges of the pleated paper to the back of each side of the dog's body.)

8. (Give each child 2 craft sticks. Show the children how to glue them on the back of each side of the dog's body. Allow the glue to dry before the children use the toy. Show the children how to hold the straw at the dog's head with one hand and make the doggie "grow" by pulling the tail end.)

9. Show me a short dog. (Children show the dog with the pleats folded up.)

10. Show me a long dog. (Children show the dog with the pleats pulled open.)

11. (You may want to teach the children a song about a dog—"Bingo," "Oh Where, Oh Where Has My Little Dog Gone?", "How Much Is That Doggie in the Window?")

BLM 55

My Turtle
Preposition
in

Materials Needed for Lesson

For each child you will need 1 copy of BLM 60,
1 sheet of construction paper, crayons, 1 craft stick, 1 brad, and glue.

Hole puncher

Cellophane tape

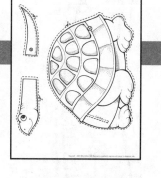

Presenting the Activity

1. (Make copies of the blackline master.)

2. **Today you are going to make a little turtle.**

3. (Give each child a copy of BLM 60.)

4. (Ask the children to color the parts of the turtle's body. When finished with the coloring, they can glue the master to a sheet of construction paper. When the glue is dry, they can cut out the turtle body parts. Children glue the turtle's head to the end of the craft stick. Punch holes as shown in the body and tail. You will need to help the children cut the slit for the turtle's head. Reinforce the back of the slit by placing a piece of tape on either side of it. Help the children attach the turtle's tail with the brad and insert the head through the slit.)

5. (Point to the body parts of the turtle and ask the children to name them.)
   Head, shell, legs, tail.

6. (Teach the children the following action poem.)

This is my turtle.	(Hold up turtle.)
He lives in a shell.	(Point to shell.)
He likes his home very well.	(Pull head in. Nod head.)
He pokes his head out	(Push head out.)
When he wants to eat.	(Push head down.)
And he pulls it back	(Pull head in.)
When he wants to sleep.	(Child closes eyes and "sleeps.")

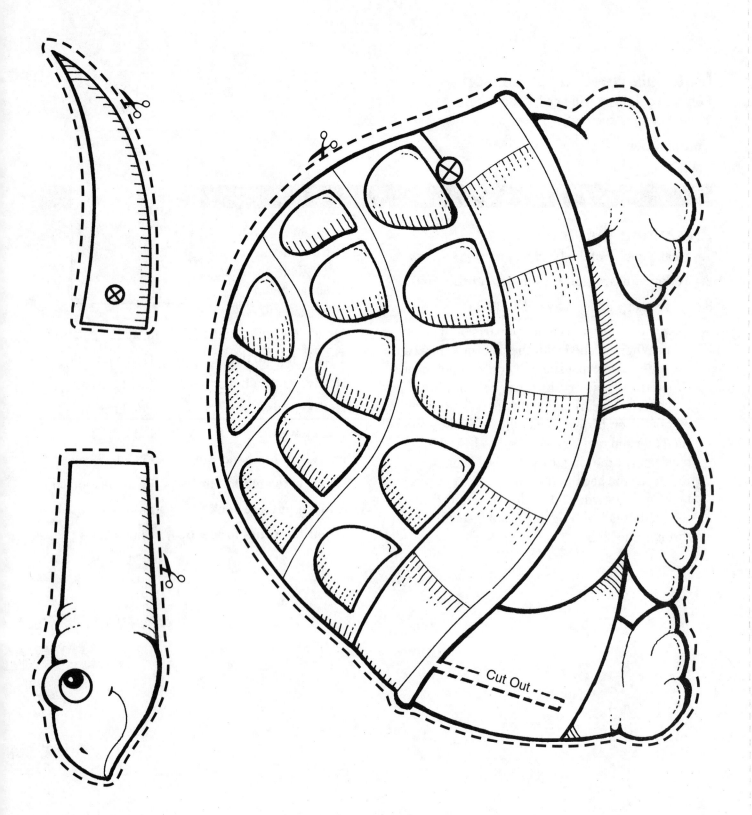

Cut Out

Animal Flip Book
Identification
Colors

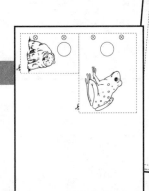

Materials Needed for Lesson

For each child you will need 1 copy of BLM 65A; 1 copy of BLM 65B; a brown, green, yellow, and red crayon; and 1 eight-inch piece of yarn.

Hole puncher

Presenting the Activity

1. (Make copies of blackline masters.)

2. Today you are going to make a book about animals and colors.

3. (Give each child a copy of BLM 65A and BLM 65B; scissors; and a brown, green, yellow, and red crayon.)

4. (Ask children to cut out the book parts along the dotted lines. Help children as needed.)

5. Find your brown crayon. Put a brown mark on the circle by the bear. ✔

   Find your green crayon. Put a green mark on the circle by the frog. ✔

   Find your yellow crayon. Put a yellow mark on the circle by the rabbit. ✔

   Find your red crayon. Put a red mark on the circle by the bird. ✔

   Now color the circles with the colors you marked. Color the animal beside the circle with the same color.

6. (Help children punch holes in the ends of the book pages and tie them together with the yarn.)

7. (Read the following poem as the children turn the pages of their books. After several readings, the children should be able to say the poem by themselves.)

   Brown bear, brown bear,
   What do you see?
   I see a green frog looking at me.
   Green frog, green frog,
   What do you see?
   I see a yellow rabbit looking at me.
   Yellow rabbit, yellow rabbit,
   What do you see?
   I see a red bird looking at me.
   Red bird, red bird, what do you see?
   I see (<u>child inserts own name</u>) looking at me!

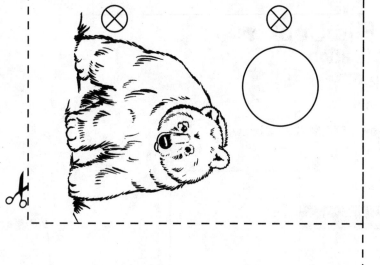

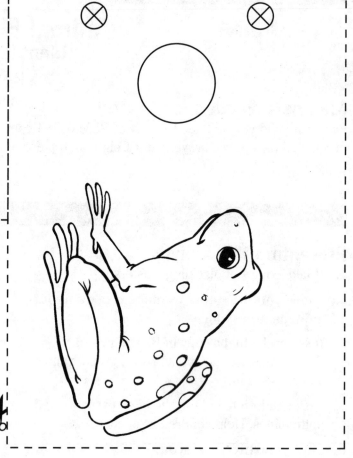

Vehicle Lotto
Object Identification

Materials Needed for Lesson

For each child you will need 1 copy of BLM 70A (and 1 copy for the teacher), 1 copy of BLM 70B, crayons, scissors, glue, paper bag, and dry beans or buttons for markers.

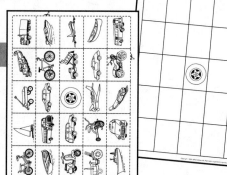

Presenting the Activity

1. (Make copies of the blackline masters.)

2. Today we are going to make a game about vehicles, and then we will play the game.

3. (Give each child a copy of BLM 70A and crayons.)

4. Remember the rule, "If it's made to take you places, it's a vehicle." What's the rule? (Signal.) *If it's made to take you places, it's a vehicle.*

   (Ask the children to identify the different vehicles. Then direct them to color the vehicles.)

5. (Give each child scissors. Direct the children to cut out the pictures of the vehicles along the dotted lines.)

6. (Give each child a copy of BLM 70B and glue. Direct the children to glue one vehicle in each blank square in any order.)

7. (To play, put the teacher's set of vehicle squares into the paper bag and give students dry beans or buttons to use for markers.)

8. Now we are ready to play the game. I'll draw one vehicle at a time out of the paper bag. You will tell me the name. (Draw a picture from the bag and show it to the children for identification.)

9. Find this vehicle on your lotto card and put a marker on it. ✔

   The center square with the wheel is a free spot. Everybody, put a marker on the center square. ✔

   The first person to mark five squares in a row gets to say, "Lotto!" But we'll keep playing until everybody gets five squares in a row.

10. (After playing the game several times, small groups of children may play Lotto independently.)

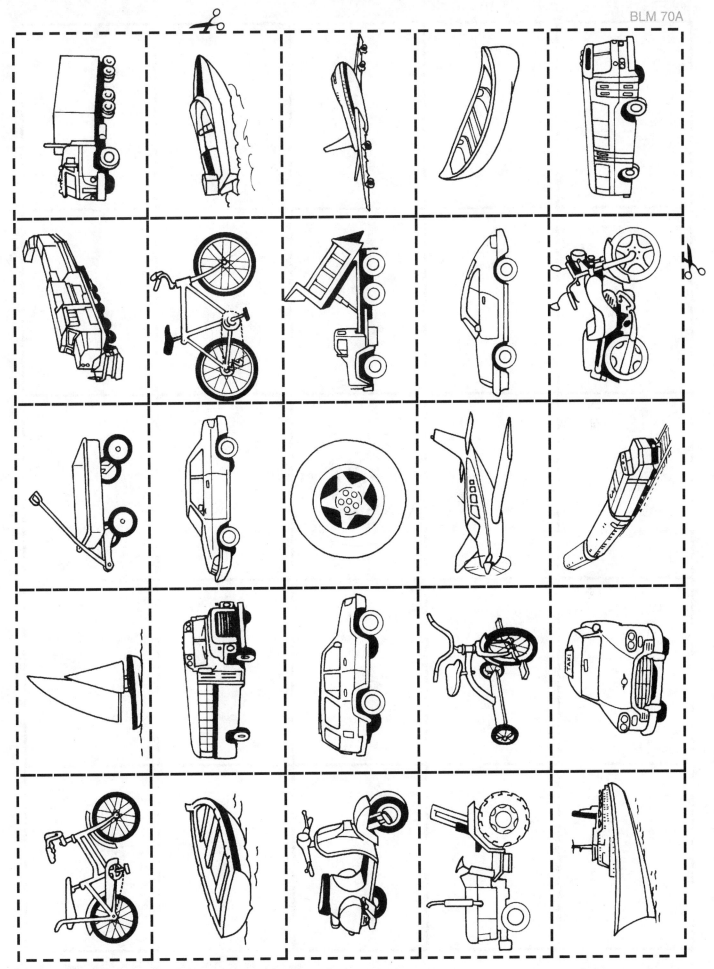

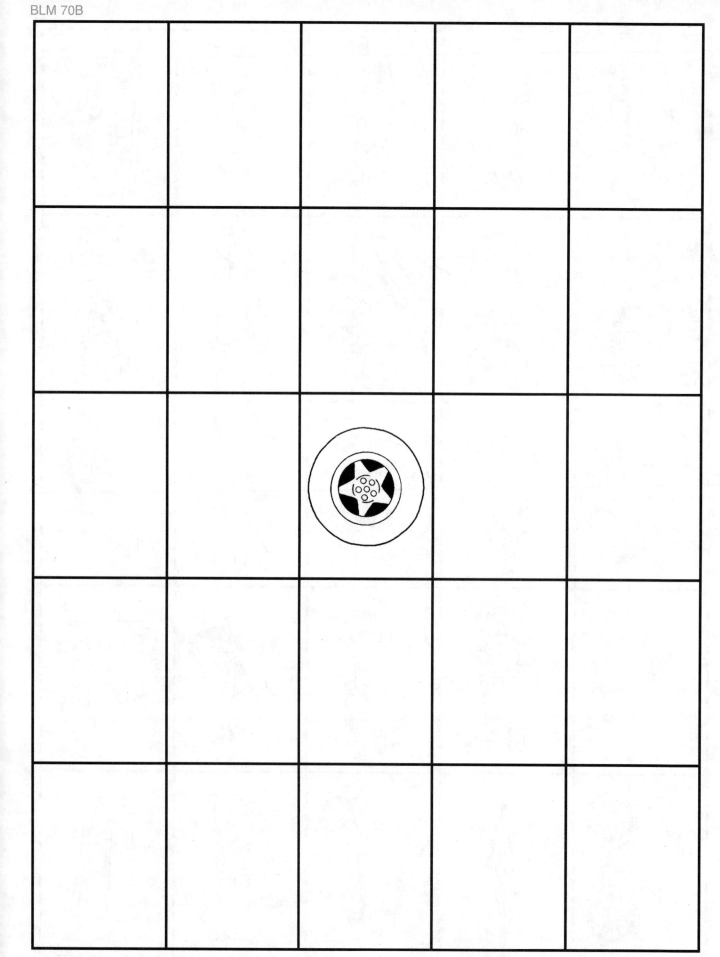

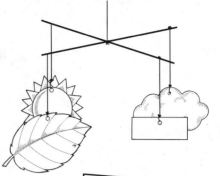

Criss-Cross Mobile
Common Information

Materials Needed for Lesson

For each child you will need 1 copy of BLM 75A, 1 copy of BLM 75B, crayons, scissors, 2 twelve-inch sticks, 4 twelve-inch pieces of yarn, 1 twenty-inch piece of yarn, and 1 6"x6" piece of blue crepe paper.

Tape or stapler

Hole puncher

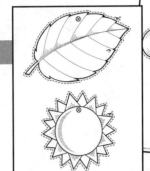

Presenting the Activity

1. (Make copies of the blackline masters. Make one mobile as an example to show the children.)

2. Today we are going to make a mobile that tells about the sky, land, sun, and clouds. (Show the children the mobile you have made.)

3. (Give each child a copy of BLM 75A and BLM 75B, scissors, and crayons.)

4. Look at the pictures. Find the sun. ✔

   What color will you make the sun? (Idea: *Yellow.*)

   Find the cloud. ✔

   What color will you make the cloud? (Ideas: *White, Gray, Blue.*)

   Find the leaf. ✔

   The leaf is for the land. What color will you make the leaf? (Idea: *Green.*)

   Find the rectangle. ✔

   The rectangle is for the sky. What color will you make the sky? (Idea: *Blue.*)

5. (Direct children to color the pictures and cut them out. Help children as needed.)

6. (Help children punch holes as shown on the patterns. Give each child a piece of blue crepe paper. Show them how to cut slashes along one edge so that the "tails" will wave in the breeze. Tape or staple the uncut edge of the crepe paper to the bottom of the rectangle.)

7. (Help the children tie the end of a twelve-inch piece of yarn to each of their pictures.)

8. (You will need to help them finish the mobile by tying together two sticks with a twenty-inch piece of yarn and attaching one picture to the end of each stick.)

9. (Children can hang the finished mobiles in the classroom and use them to review sky, land, sun, and clouds.)

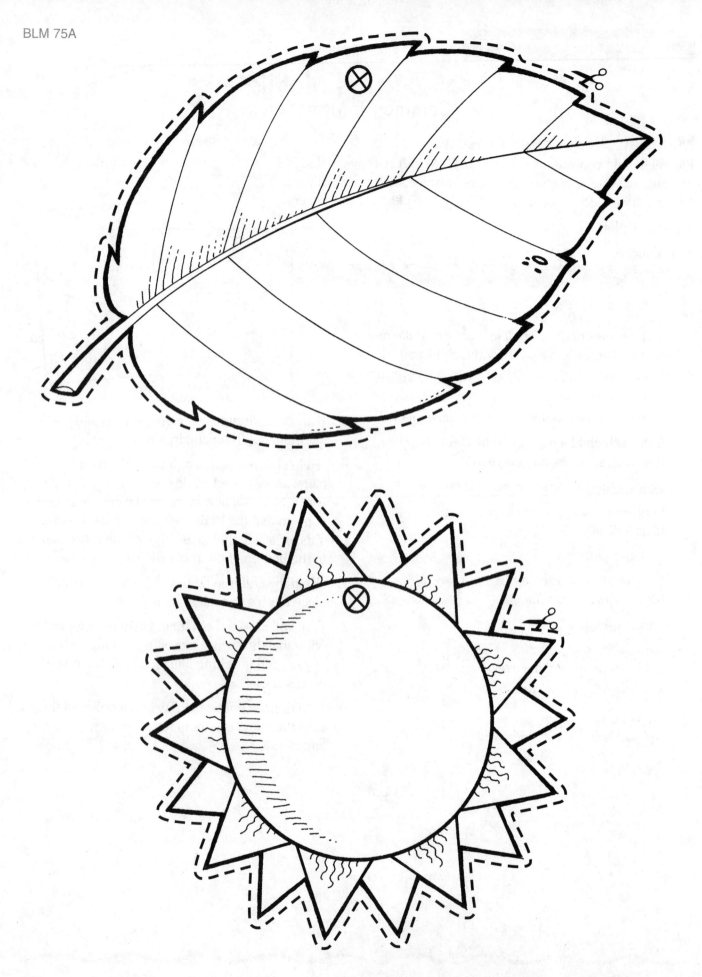

Red Light–Green Light
Common Information, Colors, Top-Middle-Bottom

Materials Needed for Lesson

For each child you will need 1 copy of BLM 80, crayons, and scissors.

1 set of six-inch circles cut from red, yellow, and green construction paper

Glue

3 tongue depressors

Presenting the Activity

1. (Make copies of the blackline master. Glue the three construction-paper circles to the tongue depressors as shown above. Color and cut out one traffic light to use as an example.)

2. **Today we are going to learn about a traffic light.** (Show the traffic light you made.)

    Who needs to pay attention to traffic lights? (Ideas: *People walking, riding bikes, driving cars, driving buses, driving trucks, etc.*)

3. **I'm going to show you the three colors that you see on a traffic light.**

    (Show the green.) **What color?** (Signal.) *Green.*

    (Show the yellow.) **What color?** (Signal.) *Yellow.*

    (Show the red.) **What color?** (Signal.) *Red.*

4. **Everybody, listen. Red means stop. What does red mean?** (Signal.) *Stop.*

    Yellow means move carefully. What does yellow mean? (Signal.) *Move carefully.*

    Green means go. What does green mean? (Signal.) *Go.*

5. **Let's do that again.** (Repeat step 4.)

6. **Here's a game we can play to see if you have learned what the traffic light colors mean.** (Line children up horizontally at a distance from you.) **When I show you a color, you'll do what the color tells you to do. What will you do if I show you green?** (Signal.) *Go.*

    What will you do if I show you red? (Signal.) *Stop.*

    What will you do if I show you yellow? (Signal.) *Move carefully.*

    Remember to walk. No running.

7. **Watch carefully.** (Show the children one of the colored circles. Change the circle after they have taken a few steps. If a player makes a mistake, he or she must go back to the starting line. Once children learn the game, they can take turns being the leader and holding the colored circles.)

8. (Give each child a copy of BLM 80, scissors, and crayons.)

9. **Now you can make your own traffic light.** (Hold up your traffic light as an example.) **What color at the top?** (Signal.) *Red.*

    Put a red mark on the top light.

    What color in the middle? (Signal.) *Yellow.*

    Put a yellow mark on the middle light.

    What color on the bottom? (Signal.) *Green.*

    Put a green mark on the bottom light.

10. **Now color and cut out your traffic light.** (Have children use their completed traffic lights to name the colors and tell what the colors mean.)

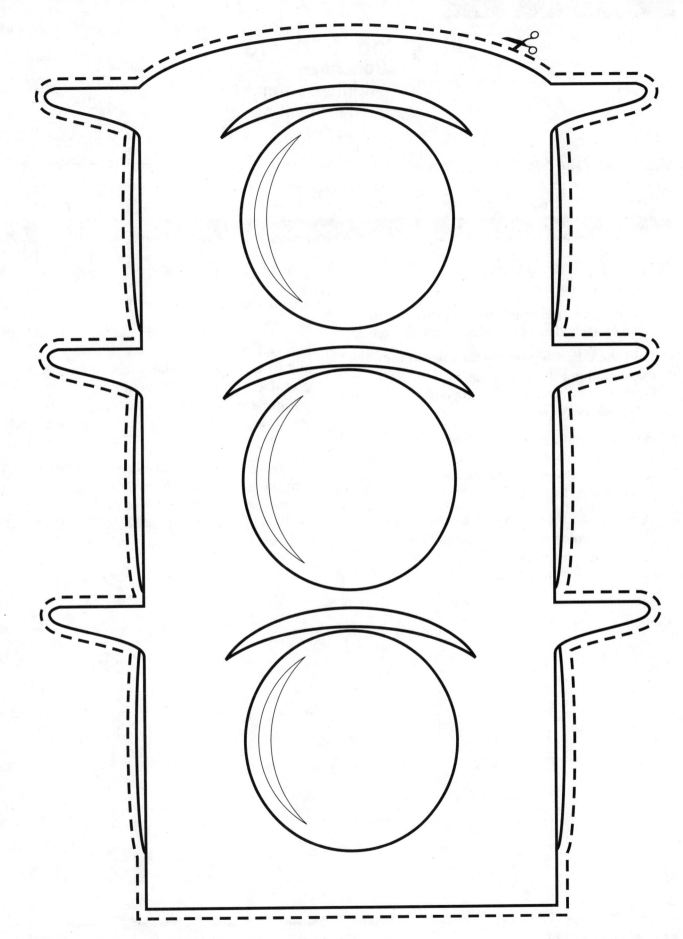

Fill Up the Refrigerator!
Containers
Top-Middle-Bottom
Object Identification
Foods

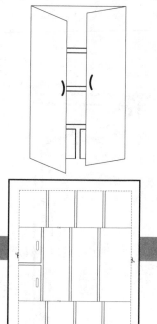

Materials Needed for Lesson

For each child you will need 1 copy of BLM 85, crayons, scissors, glue, and magazines and/or grocery store ads.

Presenting the Activity

1. (Make copies of the blackline master.)

2. Today we are going to make a refrigerator. (Give each child a copy of BLM 85 and crayons.)

3. Fold the edges of your paper toward the middle, along the dotted lines. (Demonstrate for children. Check to make sure children have folded correctly. Help as necessary.)

4. Now your refrigerator has doors. Use a crayon to make handles on the front of your refrigerator doors. (Demonstrate for children how to color handles.)

5. Open the doors of your refrigerator. Use a crayon to color the lines inside. Those are the shelves in the refrigerator. (Demonstrate for children how to color shelves.)

6. (Give each child scissors, glue, and magazines and/or grocery store ads.)

7. You can cut out pictures of food or containers of food and glue them on the shelves of your refrigerator. (Demonstrate for children how to glue a picture just above the colored shelf line of the refrigerator.)

8. (After children have finished adding items to their refrigerators, ask them to identify the contents and "Say the whole thing." For example, a child might say, *This is lettuce;* or *This is a box of ice cream.*)

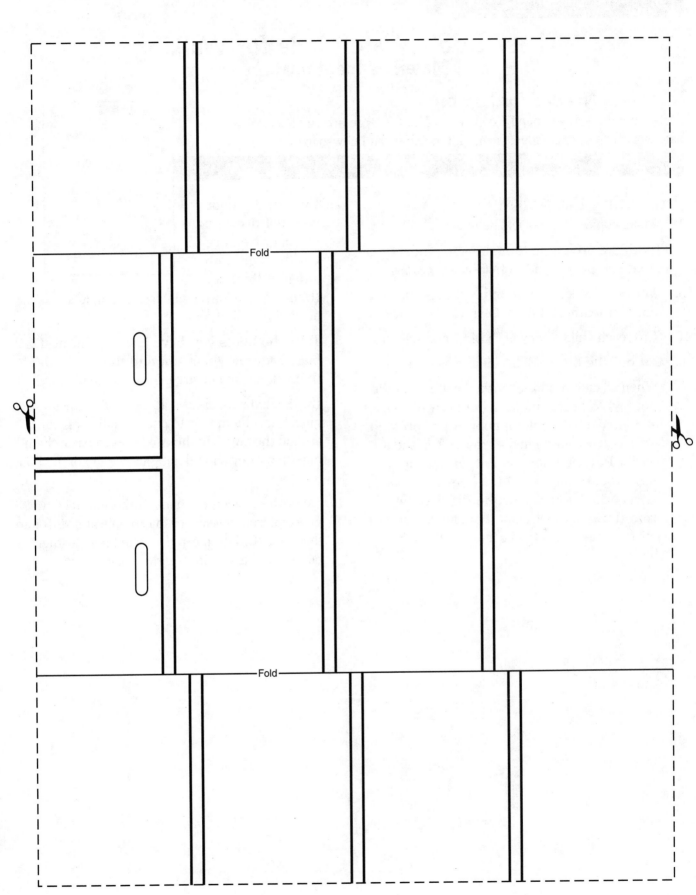

Fold

Fold

These Boots Were Made for Walking
Materials Identification

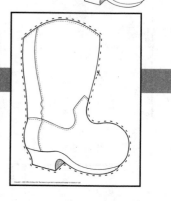

Materials Needed for Lesson

For each child you will need 1 copy of BLM 90, 1 large brown paper grocery bag, scissors, a pencil, glue, yarn, glitter, paints, and newspaper.

Presenting the Activity

1. (Make copies of the blackline master.)

2. Today we are going to make some boots. What are boots made of? (Signal.) *Leather.*

3. Can you think of some other things that are made of leather? (Ideas: *Coat, gloves, shoes.*)

4. (Give each child a copy of BLM 90 and scissors.)

5. Cut out the boot. (Help children as necessary.)

6. (When all children have finished cutting out the boot say) We can't make a boot out of real leather. We will make a boot out of pretend leather. (Give each child a grocery bag and a pencil.) Put the boot you cut out on top of your grocery bag. Hold the boot down with one hand. Use the pencil to draw a line around the boot. (Demonstrate for children how to trace around the boot template. Help children as necessary.)

7. Cut out the boot you just drew on the bag. Be sure to cut through both sides of the bag. (Demonstrate for the children and help as needed.)

8. Take the boots you have just cut out of the bag. Crumple them up, and then smooth them flat. (Demonstrate for the children.)

9. (Each child should have access to a bottle of glue. Show them how to put a thin line of glue around the edges of the two boots to paste them together. They should not glue the top of the boot together.)

10. (After the glue on the boots is thoroughly dry, give children newspaper to crumple and stuff into the boots. Children can decorate their "leather" boots with yarn, glitter, and/or paint.)

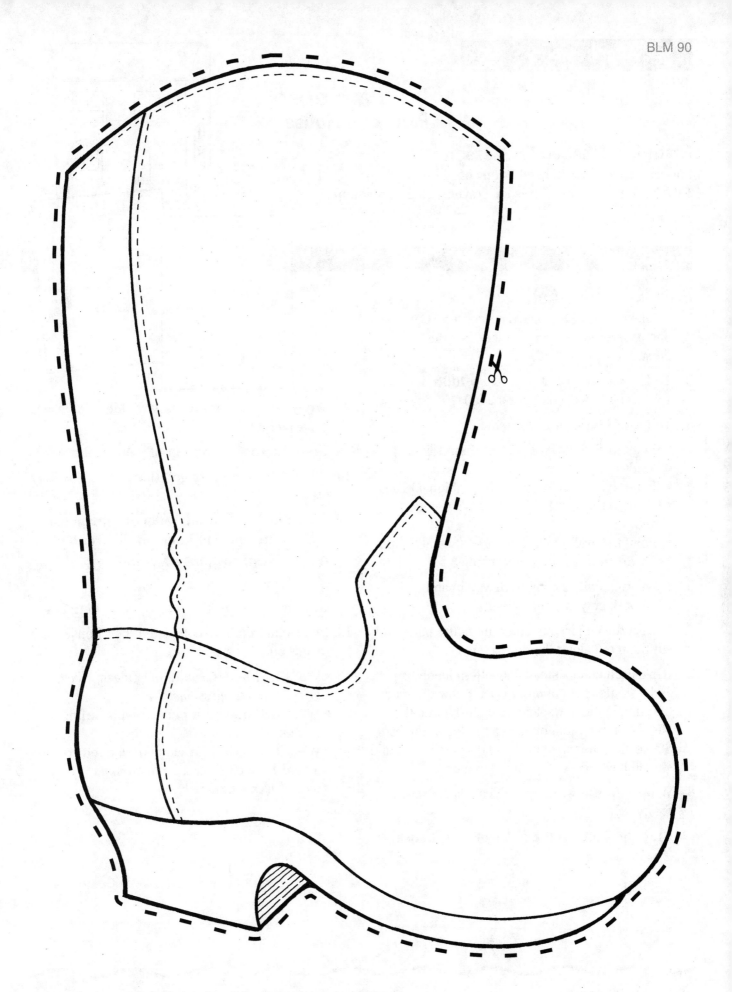

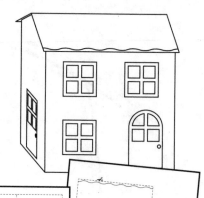

Build a House
Parts of a House

Materials Needed for Lesson

For each child you will need 1 copy of BLM 95A, 1 copy of BLM 95B, 1 flat-bottom lunch bag, scissors, crayons, glue, and newspaper.

Stapler

Presenting the Activity

1. (Make copies of the blackline masters. Complete one paper house as an example. See the illustration above.)

2. Today we are going to make a little house. (Show the house you have made.)

3. Tell me the parts of a house.

   • (Point to a window.) What is this? (Signal.) *Window.*

   • (Point to a door.) What is this? (Signal.) *Door.*

   • (Point to the roof.) What is this? (Signal.) *Roof.*

   • (Point to a wall.) What is this? (Signal.) *Wall.*

4. Let's do that again. (Repeat step 3.)

5. (Give each child a copy of BLM 95A and BLM 95B, crayons, and scissors.)

6. (Direct the children to color the house parts and cut them out along the dotted lines.)

7. (Give each child a small flat-bottom lunch bag and a single sheet of newspaper. Show them how to crumple the newspaper and stuff it into the bag. They can then fold down the top of the bag. Staple shut the top of each child's bag. Each child should have access to a bottle of glue.)

8. Where do the walls go? (Idea: *On the sides of the house.*)

   Glue the walls to the sides of your house. ✔

9. Where do the roof parts go? (Idea: *On top of the house.*)

   Glue the roof to the top of your house. ✔

10. Where do the doors go? (Idea: *On the walls of the house.*)

    Glue the doors to the walls of your house— one on the back and one on the front. ✔

11. Where do the windows go? (Idea: *On the walls of the house.*)

    Glue windows to the wall of your house. ✔

12. (After children have completed their houses, ask review questions such as:)

    • What is a house made of? (Ideas: *Wood, brick, concrete, glass, metal.*)

    • What do you call a person who builds things out of wood? *Carpenter.*

    • What tools would a carpenter need to build a real house? (Ideas: *Drill, hammer, screwdriver, paintbrush, saw.*)

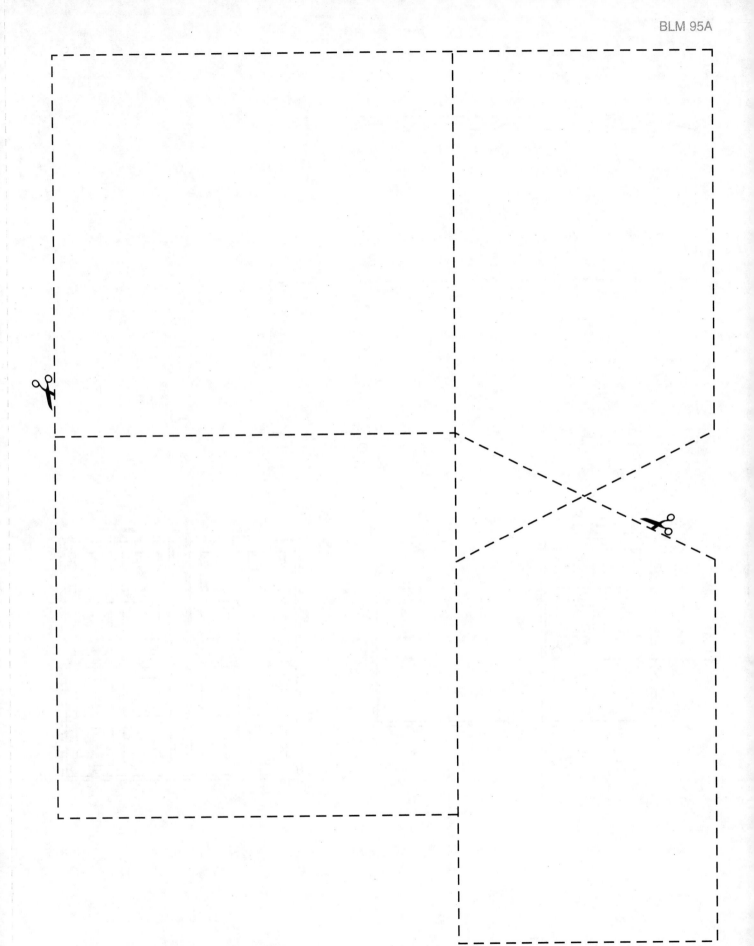

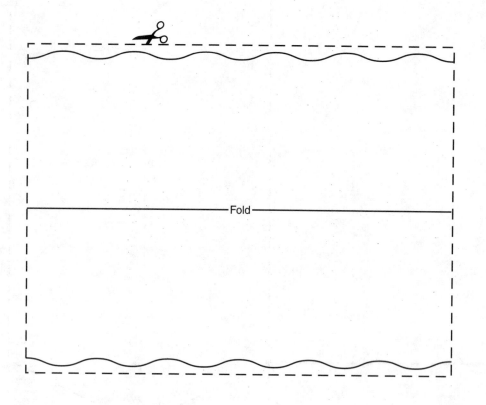

Fold

Carpenter with Tools
Occupation
Tools

Materials Needed for Lesson

For each child you will need 1 copy of BLM 100A, 1 copy of BLM 100B copied on card stock, 1 sheet of 8½" x 11" cardboard, crayons, scissors, glue, and 5 pieces of hook-and-loop tape cut into ½" pieces.

Presenting the Activity

1. (Make copies of the blackline masters. Complete one carpenter picture as an example. See illustration above.)

2. (Show the children the carpenter you have made.)

   What do we call a person who builds things out of wood? (Signal.) *A carpenter.*

3. **Today you are going to make a carpenter and some tools a carpenter uses.** (Give each child a copy of BLM 100A and crayons. Direct the children to color the carpenter. Give each child a sheet of cardboard and glue. Children should glue the picture of the carpenter to the cardboard.)

4. (Give each child a copy of BLM 100B, crayons, and scissors. Direct the children to color the tools and cut them out. Give each child five loop pieces of hook-and-loop tape and two hook pieces of hook-and-loop tape. Show them how to glue the hook pieces to the carpenter's hands with the hook-side out. Then they will glue one loop piece to the back of each tool with the loop-side out. Help children as necessary.)

5. (Show the children how they can change the tools in the carpenter's hands.)

6. (Ask the children to tell you what tools the carpenter has and "Say the whole thing." For example, they might say, *The carpenter has a hammer and a nail.* After the children have played the game several times, they can play the game with a partner or in a small group.)

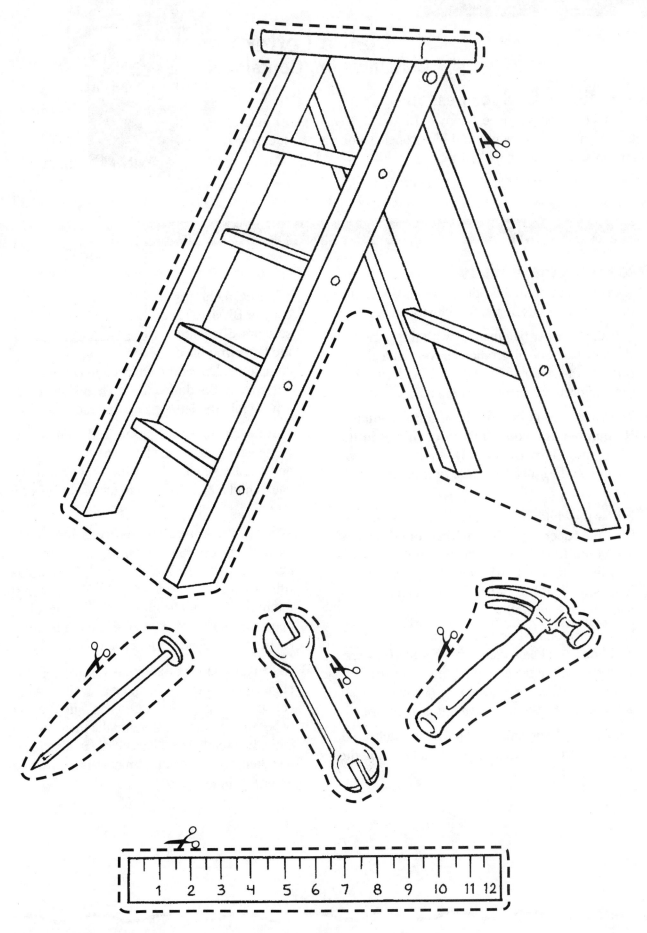

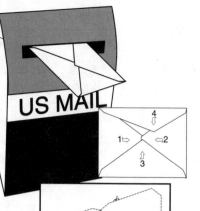

Mail a Letter
Classification, Containers

Materials Needed for Lesson

For each child you will need 1 copy of BLM 105, 1 small paper lunch bag, 1 quarter sheet of red, white, and blue construction paper, glue, scissors, and magazines to cut up for pictures.

1 large paper grocery bag, 1 sheet each of red, white, and blue construction paper, tape

Presenting the Activity

1. (Make copies of the blackline master. Complete one letter as an example. See illustration above.)

2. (Make the paper bag mailbox with the large grocery bag. See illustration above. Cut a slot through the red piece and the bag underneath so that children can insert their "mail.")

3. **Today we are going to talk about a container. Remember the rule. If you put things in it, it's a container. Everybody, say the rule with me.** (Signal.) *If you put things in it, it's a container.*

4. (Show the children the mailbox you have made from the paper bag.) **This is the container we are going to talk about today. You might see one like this on a sidewalk. You can put letters in it. What is it?** (Call on a child.) *A mailbox.* **Yes, a mailbox.**

5. **What happens when you put a letter in a mailbox?** (Call on a child. Ideas: *A mail carrier takes the mail to the post office; it goes by truck, train, or airplane to another city; the letter is delivered to the person to whom it is addressed.*)

6. (Discuss with the children how mail is delivered. Tell them they will make a letter and put it in the classroom mailbox.)

7. (Give each child a copy of BLM 100 and scissors. Show them the letter you have completed. Direct the children to cut out their letter along the dotted lines. Then show them how to fold the letter along the fold lines.)

8. (Give each child a magazine. Tell them to find a picture they especially like. They can cut it out and put it inside the letter they have made. Give each child a piece of tape to tape shut his or her letter.)

9. **What is the container we are going to put something in?** (Signal.) *Mailbox.* (Direct children to deposit their letters in the mailbox. After each child has deposited a letter, open the top of the bag and let each child choose a letter to open. Or you can choose one child to be the mail carrier who delivers a letter to each child.)

10. (As an alternative or additional activity, give each child a paper lunch bag and red, white, and blue construction paper. Children can glue the colored paper to the lunch bag and make their own individual mailboxes. These little mailboxes may be taken home. Children may want to insert a letter for their family.)

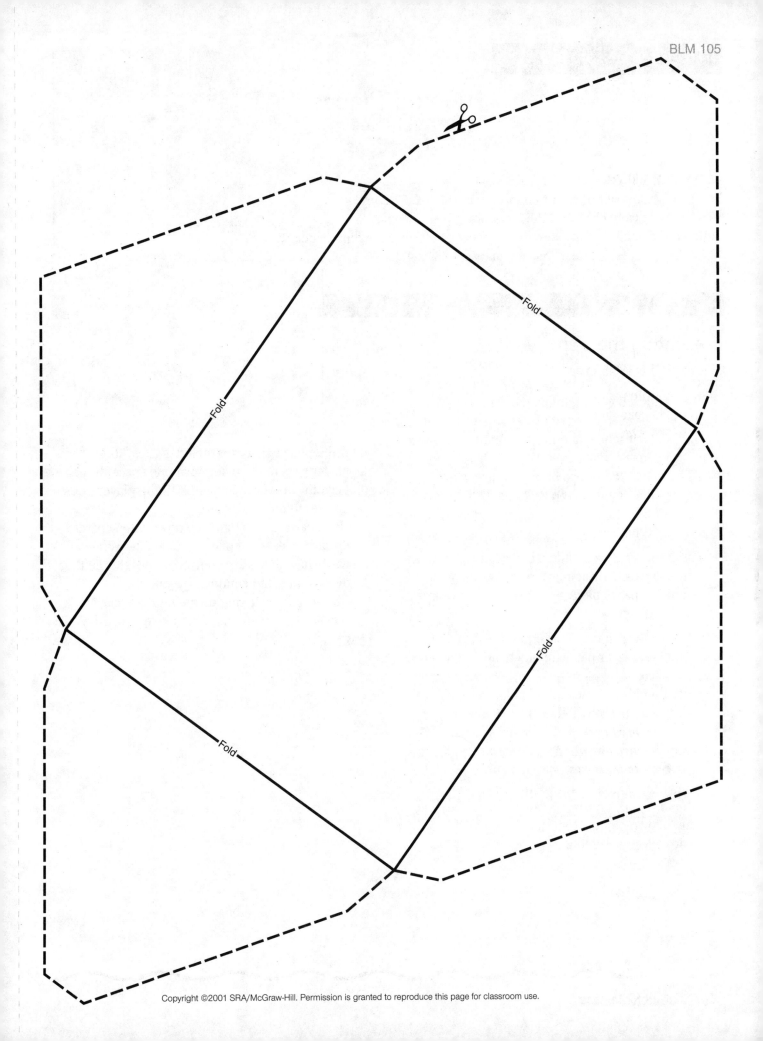

Fold

Fold

Fold

Fold

Going Places
Vehicles
Locations

Materials Needed for Lesson

For each group of two to four children you will need 1 copy of BLM 110A, 1 copy of BLM 110B, scissors, glue, crayons, buttons or dry beans for markers, 10 pieces of red construction paper (3" x 4"), 5 pieces of blue construction paper (3" x 4"), and 1 piece of cardboard (8 ½" x 11").

Presenting the Activity

1. (Make 1 copy of each blackline master for each group of two to four children. You may wish to have children color the game pieces and game board. Cut out the game pieces along the dotted lines. Glue each locations piece to a 3" x 4" piece of red construction paper. Glue each vehicles piece to a 3" x 4" piece of blue construction paper. Glue the game board to an 8 ½" x 11" piece of cardboard.)

2. (Divide the class into groups of two to four children. Give each child a dry bean or button to use as a marker. Each group will need a game board and a complete set of red and blue cards. To play the game:

   • Each player puts a marker on the start line.
   • The first player picks up one blue card and one red card.
   • After looking at the cards, the player makes a statement about whether the pictures go together. For example, if pictures of a school and bike are drawn, the player can say, *Yes, a bike can take me to school.* If pictures of a bike and the jungle are drawn, the player can say, *No, a bike can't take me to the jungle.* Players are allowed to talk together to decide if two cards can go together.

   • If the player's answer includes "Yes," the player gets to move forward one space. If the player's answer includes "No," the player does not get to move forward.
   • Used cards should go face down into separate discard piles—red pile and blue pile. When all cards have been drawn from a pile, shuffle the discard pile and continue playing.
   • Children keep taking turns until one player crosses the finish line. That player wins the game.)

FINISH

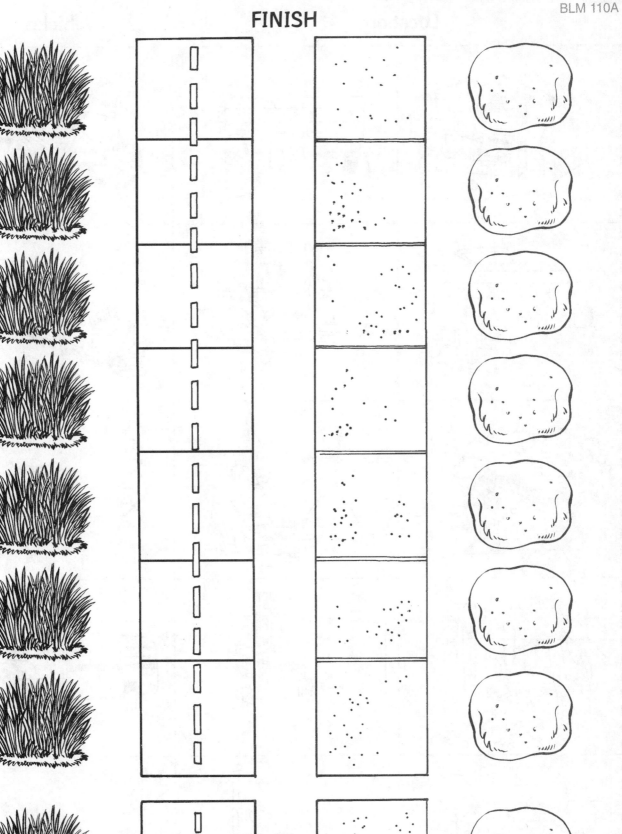

START

Locations

Vehicles

Following the Leader
First-Next-Last

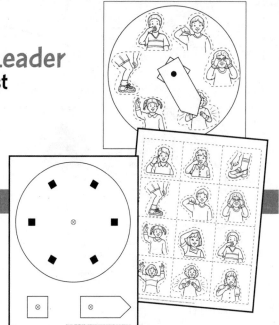

Materials Needed for Lesson

2 copies of BLM 115A, 1 copy of BLM 115B, scissors, glue, 2 pieces of cardboard (8½" x 11"), crayons, 2 paper fasteners, hole puncher

Presenting the Activity

1. (Make 2 copies of blackline masters. You may wish to have children color the game boards and actions pictures. Glue copies of BLM 115A to cardboard. Cut out the pieces. Punch holes as shown in the game board, arrow, and spacer. Attach an arrow to each game board with the spacer between the board and arrow. Choose six action pictures to glue to each game board.)

2. (To play the game:

    • Choose a game board to use.
    • The first player spins the arrow. That player says the action, such as *Touch your nose.* The group must perform the action.
    • The second player spins the arrow. That player says the action, such as *Clap your hands.* The group must perform that action.
    • The third player spins the arrow. That player says the action, such as *Touch your head.* The group must perform that action.
    • After the third action has been completed, you say) **First!** (Children perform first action—Touch nose. You say) **Next!** (Children perform second action—Clap hands. You say) **Last!** (Children perform third action—Touch head.)
    • (You say) **Go!** (Children perform each action in order—Touch nose, clap hands, touch head.)

3. (Continue the game until all players have been able to spin an action. You may wish to use the second game board for another round of play.)

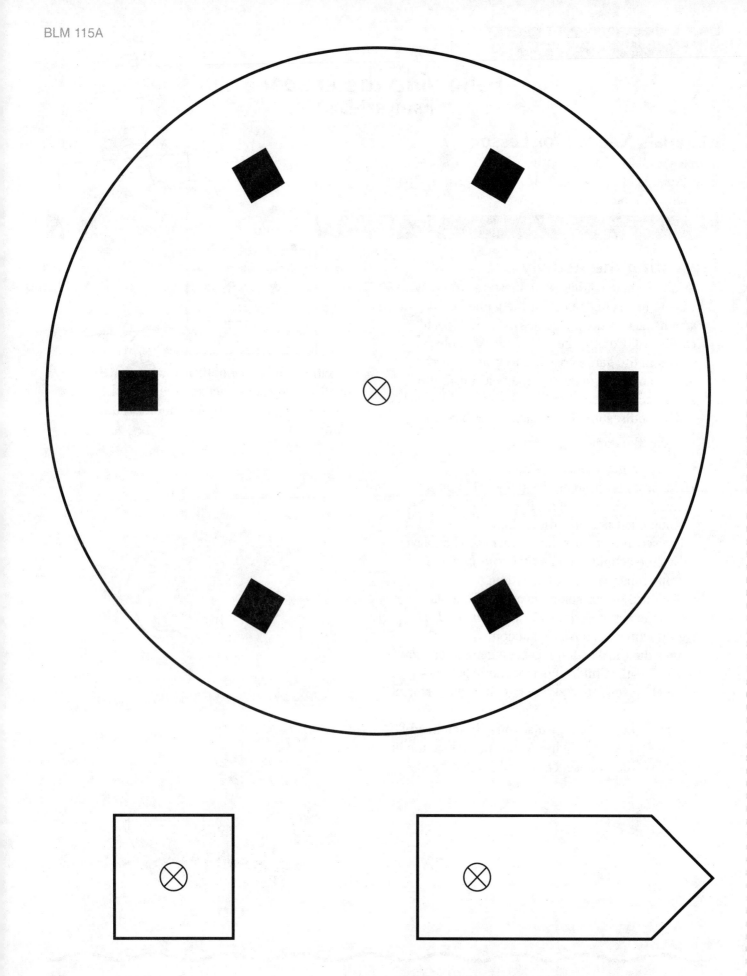

Cover Up!
Opposites

Materials Needed for Lesson
1 copy of BLM 120A, 1 copy of BLM 120B, crayons, scissors

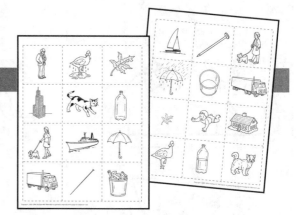

Presenting the Activity

1. (Make copies of the blackline masters. You may wish to have children color the game board and game cards. Cut out the game cards.)

2. Listen. If something is not wet, it is the opposite of wet, so it's dry. If something is not big, it's the opposite of big. So what do you know about it? (Signal.) *It's small.*

3. Today we are going to play a game with opposites. I'll show you a picture. You have to choose the opposite of that picture. If I show you a picture of a person who is old, you will show me a picture of a person who is young. Young is the opposite of old. If I show you a picture of a person who is young, what picture will you show me? (Signal.) *A picture of a person who is old.*

   Yes, old is the opposite of young.

   If I show you a picture of an animal that is small, what picture will you show me? (Signal.) *A picture of an animal that is big.*

   Yes, big is the opposite of small.

4. (Turn all the game cards face down on the table and scramble them. The first player draws a card and must talk about the picture and its opposite. For example, the child might say, *Empty is the opposite of full.* The child then places the card on its opposite on the game board. The game continues until all spots on the game card are covered.)

Happy/Sad Puppet
Opposites, Happy/Sad

Materials Needed for Lesson

For each child you will need 1 copy of BLM 125, crayons, scissors, 1 tongue depressor, and glue.

Presenting the Activity

1. (Make copies of the blackline master. Make one bear puppet as an example.)

2. **I'll show you how I look when I'm happy.** (Smile.)

   Now I'll show you how I look when I'm sad. (Make a sad face.)

3. **Your turn. Show me how you look when you're happy.** (Signal. Children smile.)

   Show me how you look when you're sad. (Signal. Children make a sad face.)

4. **Listen. The opposite of happy is sad. What's the opposite of happy?** (Signal.) *Sad.*

   The opposite of sad is happy. What's the opposite of sad? (Signal.) *Happy.*

5. **Today we are going to make a puppet. The puppet will be able to show us a happy face or a sad face.**

6. (Give each child a copy of BLM 125, crayons, and scissors. Direct the children to color one bear with a sad face and one bear with a happy face. Show the children the example you have made.)

7. (Give each child a tongue depressor and glue. Show them how to glue the tongue depressor to the back of one bear head, then glue the other bear head to the back of the first one. Show them the puppet you have made as an example. Help children as necessary.)

8. **Now we are ready to play with our puppets. Make your puppet do what I say.**

   • **Show me a happy face.** (Children should show the happy face of the puppet.)

   • **Show me a sad face.** (Children should show the sad face of the puppet.)

   • **Listen. Show me the opposite of a happy face.** (Children should show the sad face of the puppet.)

   • **Show me the opposite of a sad face.** (Children should show the happy face of the puppet.)

9. **Listen. The bear is happy. Say that sentence.** (Signal.) *The bear is happy.*

   Here's the sentence that tells the opposite about the bear: The bear is sad. Say that sentence. (Signal.) *The bear is sad.*

10. **Now, show me the happy bear and say the sentence.** (Signal. Children show happy face of the bear.) *The bear is happy.*

11. **Now show me the sad bear and say the sentence.** (Signal. Children show sad face of the bear.) *The bear is sad.*

12. **Now, I'll make it harder. Be careful. Show me the opposite of sad and say the sentence.** (Signal. Children show the happy face.) *The bear is happy.*

13. **Show me the opposite of happy and say the sentence.** (Signal. Children show the sad face.) *The bear is sad.*

14. (Children can continue playing the game with a partner or in a small group with one child as leader.)

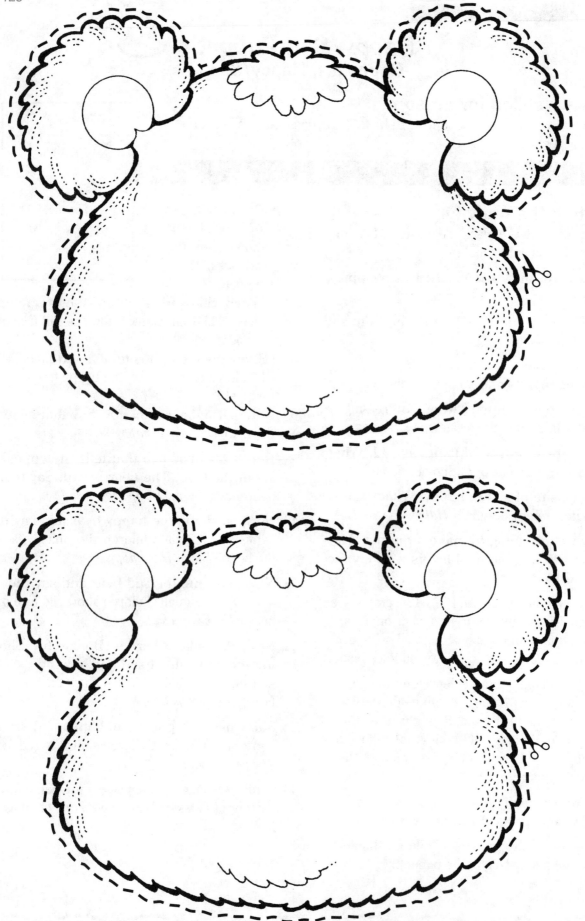

Animal Babies on the Farm
Classification
Animals

Materials Needed for Lesson

For each child you will need 1 copy of BLM 130A, 1 copy of BLM 130B (and 1 copy for the teacher), crayons, and scissors.

Presenting the Activity

1. (Make copies of the blackline masters. Complete one set of baby animal pictures from BLM 130B to use for the game.)

2. **Today we are going to make a game to play with farm animals. What do we call a place where food is grown?** (Signal.) *A farm.*

3. (Give each child a copy of BLM 130A.) **Here's a picture of a farm. I'll name some of the things in the picture, and you touch them.** (Name the following items, and check to make sure children are touching them as they are named: cow, sheep, cat, chickens, horse, dog, goose, pig, farmer, tractor, barn, house, field.)

4. (Give each child crayons. Have children color the farm picture. When children are finished, hold up a copy of BLM 130A. Point to each item and ask the children to name it, find it on their picture, and "Say the whole thing." For example, when you point to the horse, the children should touch the horse and say, *This is a horse.*)

5. (Give each child a copy of BLM 130B, crayons, and scissors.) **Here are pictures of baby farm animals. Color the pictures and cut them out.**

6. (Shuffle your set of baby animal pictures and turn them face down on the table.) **Now we are going to play the game. I'll turn over one picture at a time. You have to tell me the name of the animal.** (Turn over one card for the children to identify.) **Now find the same baby animal in your cards.** (Children find the matching card in their set.) **Put the baby animal on top of its parent on your farm picture.** (Children find the matching parent animal and lay the baby on it. Continue the game until all baby animal pictures have been identified and put on top of their parents.)

7. (If children are able to learn new vocabulary, introduce the baby animal names. Say, for example, "A baby cow is called a calf." [sheep–lamb, pig–piglet, cat–kitten, dog–puppy, chicken–chick, horse–foal, goose–gosling, cow–calf]

Shop Till You Drop!
Classification
Food
Location

Materials Needed for Lesson

For each child you will need 1 copy of BLM 135A, 1 copy of BLM 135B, crayons, glue, 1 small paper lunch bag, scissors, and magazines and/or grocery store ads.

Presenting the Activity

1. (Make copies of the blackline masters.)

2. **Today we are going to talk about a place where you go to buy food.** (Show the children a copy of BLM 135A.) **What is this place?** (Call on a child. Idea: *A grocery store.*)

   Yes, a grocery store. Everybody, what is this place? (Signal.) *A grocery store.*

3. (Give each child a copy of BLM 135A. Discuss the items shown in the picture—clerk, customers, cash register, shelves, cart, groceries. Give the children crayons and have them color the picture of the grocery store.)

4. (After children have finished coloring, ask them to touch the following items in the picture as you name them—clerk, customers, cash register, shelves, cart, groceries.)

5. **What does the customer put the groceries in while shopping?** (Call on a child. Idea: *A cart.*)

   Yes, a cart. Everybody, touch the cart. ✔

6. **Today we are going to take a pretend trip to a grocery store. Everybody will get a cart and fill it with groceries.** (Give each child a copy of BLM 135B, crayons, a small brown lunch bag, scissors, and glue. Direct the children to color the cart, cut it out along the dashed lines, and glue it on the front of the lunch bag.)

7. (Give each child a magazine and/or newspaper grocery store ad. Direct children to cut out pictures of food items and "put them in the cart.")

8. (Ask children to take out their "grocery purchases" one-at-a-time and share them with the group or a partner. The child should "Say the whole thing" about the purchase. For example, a child might say, *This is ice cream. This is cereal.*)

SALE

2.40

Occupation Concentration
Occupations
Related Objects

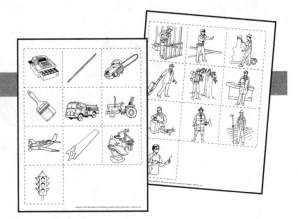

Materials Needed for Lesson

1 copy of BLM 140A, 1 copy of BLM 140B, 2 pieces of cardboard (8½" x 11"), glue, crayons, scissors

Presenting the Activity

1. (Make copies of the blackline masters. You may wish to have children color the game cards. Glue the BLMs to cardboard and cut out the cards.)

2. Today we are going to play a concentration game with some cards. *Concentration* means that you need to think about and remember what you have seen. Some of the cards will show pictures of people working. Some of the cards will show pictures of tools people use when they are working. You will try to match the people to the tools they need on their jobs. (Show the children each of the cards and ask one child to "Say the whole thing" about each card. For example, a child might say, *This is a firefighter.* Then show the children how to make a match between two cards, for example a firefighter and a hose.)

3. (To begin the game, lay the cards facedown on the table. At first, place all the occupation cards in one row and all the work-related items in another row.

   The first player draws two cards, one from each row. The player must "Say the whole thing" about the pictures. For example, the player might say, *This is a firefighter. This is a hose.* If the cards match, the player gets to keep the cards and continue playing. If the cards don't match, the player puts them facedown back in the same spots.

The next player draws two cards and the game continues until all cards are drawn and matched. The player who has the most cards at the end of the game is the winner.

The children will soon discover that if they can remember where certain cards are, they will be able to match them more quickly. You may wish to start the game with only four sets of matching cards.

After children learn the game, you may increase the number of cards in each row. Eventually, you can make the game even more difficult by laying all of the cards facedown in random order.)

How Absurd! Flip Book
Jungle
Animals
Absurdities

Materials Needed for Lesson

For each child you will need 1 copy of BLM 145A, 1 copy of BLM 145B, crayons, and scissors.

Stapler

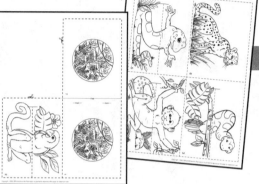

Presenting the Activity

1. (Make copies of the blackline masters.)

2. **What do we call a forest in a hot place?** (Signal.) *A jungle.*

   What would you find in a jungle? (Call on individual children. Accept reasonable responses.)

3. **Today we are going to make a book about some animals that live in the jungle.** (Give each child a copy of BLM 145A and BLM 145B and crayons.)

4. **Here are some pictures we will put in our books. Remember the rule that if something is absurd, it is very silly. What do we call something that is very silly?** (Signal.) *Absurd.*

5. **Do you see anything absurd about some of these pictures?** (Idea: *Yes.*)

6. (Discuss what is wrong with each picture. Encourage the children to guess what two animals are represented in the top and bottom part of each picture.)

7. (Discuss with the children what colors the animals would be. Direct the children to color the animals. After the children have finished coloring, give each child scissors and show them how to cut the book pages apart along the dotted lines. Help the children assemble the books as shown in the example. The jungle picture should appear on the front and the back. Staple the book on the left margin. Help the children cut the inside pages along the midline.)

8. (Children can "read" their books to a partner, turning half pages at a time and explaining why parts of the jungle animals are absurd.)

7

Fold

Staple   Staple

2   1

5

6

4

3

Make Believe Menu
Location
Occupation
Vocabulary

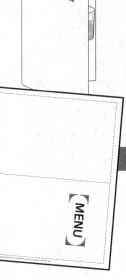

Materials Needed for Lesson
For each child you will need 1 copy of BLM 150A, 1 copy of BLM 150B, scissors, glue, and magazines and/or grocery store ads.

Presenting the Activity

1. (Make copies of the blackline masters.)

2. **What do we call a place where you go to buy a meal?** (Signal.) *A restaurant.*

3. (Show the children a copy of BLM 150A.) **Here's a picture of a restaurant. I'll point to some of the things in the restaurant. You tell me what they are.**

   - (Point to a waiter.) **Who is this?** (Signal.) *A waiter.*
     What does a waiter do? (Idea: *Serves food to customers in a restaurant.*)
   - (Point to the menu.) **What is this?** (Signal.) *A menu.*
     What is a menu for? (Idea: *Tells you what kinds of food the restaurant has.*)
   - (Point to the cashier.) **Who is this?** (Signal.) *A cashier.*
     What does a cashier do? (Idea: *Takes the money.*)
   - (Point to the cash register.) **What is this?** (Signal.) *A cash register.*
     What is a cash register for? (Idea: *The place the cashier puts the money.*)
   - (Point to the cook.) **Who is this?** (Signal.) *A cook.*
     What does the cook do? (Idea: *Cooks the food.*)

4. (Give each child a copy of BLM 150A and crayons. Direct the children to color the picture of the restaurant. After children have finished coloring, repeat step 3. Have the children find the items in the picture they have completed.)

5. (Give each child a copy of BLM 150B.) **What is this?** (Idea: *A menu.*)

   What is missing from the menu? (Idea: *The food.*)

6. (Give each child scissors, glue, and magazines and/or newspaper grocery store ads. Direct children to use the magazines and/or ads to find pictures of food items they would like to put on their restaurant menus. They can cut out the pictures of food and glue them on their menus.)

7. (Children can play "restaurant" with their menus. Have them trade menus. One child can be the "waiter" and several others can be the "customers." The "customers" can order dinner from the menus. Children can make statements when they order. For example, a child might say, *I'll have a hamburger.*)

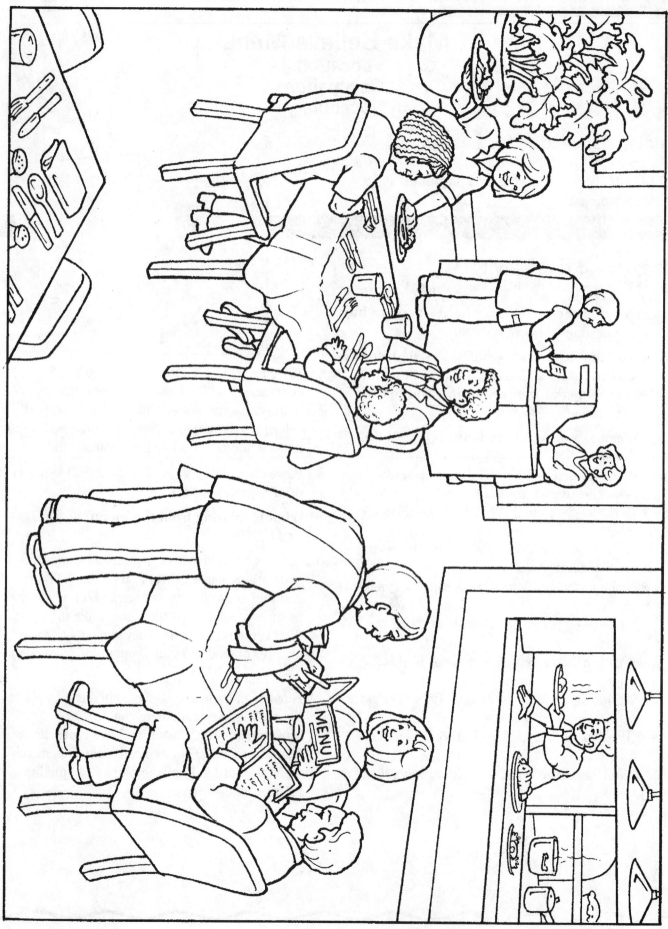

MENU

School-Home Link
Newsletter 1

Some New Words We've Learned

Names

Your child has been learning names:

- First name
- Name of teacher
- Name of school
- Names of other children in class

Other Words

Here are some other words your child has learned:

- table
- chair
- broom
- bottle
- cup
- book

Activity Update

We played the "Object Concentration Game." We matched pictures of trees, cats, dogs, shoes, boys, and girls. Play this game with your child using the cards he or she brings home. Here's how to play:

1. Turn the cards facedown.

2. The first player turns over two cards. If the cards match, the player says what the picture is, keeps the cards, and takes another turn.

3. If the cards do not match, the player turns the cards back over and the next player takes a turn.

4. The game continues until all cards are matched.

5. Encourage your child to say a sentence when naming an object. For example: "This is a dog."

Things to Talk About at Home

Your Child's First Name

Have your child practice saying, "My name is _____." Later your child will learn to say his or her last name.

Teacher's Name

Tell your child the teacher's name. Have your child practice saying, "My teacher's name is _____."

Name of School

Tell your child the name of the school. Ask, "What's the name of your school?" Have your child practice saying, "My school is _____."

Language Fun

Here's a little poem you and your child can learn in English and Spanish.

Hello!
Hello, hello!
Hello, and
  How are you?
I'm fine,
I'm fine,
And I hope that
  you are, too!

¡Hola!
¡Hola, hola!
Hola y
  ¿cómo estás?
Estoy bien,
estoy bien,
y ¡espero que
  estés bien, también!

Spanish Time

Here's a song you can sing with your child. Sing it to the tune of "Frère Jacques."

  Buenos días, buenos días,
  ¿cómo estás? ¿cómo estás?
  Muy bien, gracias,
  Muy bien, gracias,
  ¿y usted? ¿y usted?

  Buenas noches, buenas noches,
  ¿cómo estás? ¿cómo estás?
  Muy bien, gracias,
  muy bien, gracias,
  ¿y usted? ¿y usted?

Conexión con la escuela y la casa
Boletín 1

Algunas palabras que hemos aprendido

Nombres

Su hijo ha aprendido los nombres:

- Nombre
- Nombre del maestro
- Nombre de la escuela
- Nombres de otros niños de la clase

Otras palabras

Éstas son otras palabras que su hijo ha aprendido:

- table
- chair
- broom
- bottle
- cup
- book

Actividades de última hora

Jugamos el juego "Concentrarse en el objeto."
Hicimos coincidir ilustraciones de árboles, gatos,
perros, zapatos, niños y niñas. Juegue este juego
con su hijo y use las cartas que él o ella lleve a la
casa. Así es como se juega:

1. Coloque las cartas boca abajo.

2. El primer jugador voltea dos cartas. Si coinciden
   las cartas, el jugador tiene que decir cuál es la
   ilustración, tomar las cartas y volver a jugar.

3. Si no coinciden las cartas, el jugador voltea las
   cartas boca abajo y le toca jugar al siguiente
   jugador.

4. El juego sigue hasta que se hagan coincidir
   todas las cartas.

5. Anime a su hijo a que diga una oración cuando
   nombre el objeto. Por ejemplo: "Éste es un
   perro."

Cosas sobre qué conversar en el hogar

El nombre de su hijo

Pida a su hijo que practique diciendo, "Mi nombre
es _____." Luego, su hijo aprenderá a decir su
apellido.

El nombre del maestro

Dígale a su hijo el nombre del maestro. Pídale que
practique diciendo, "El nombre de mi maestro
es _____."

El nombre de la escuela

Dígale a su hijo el nombre de la escuela.
Pregúntele, "¿Cuál es el nombre de tu escuela?"
Pídale que practique diciendo, "Mi escuela es
_____."

Diviértete con el lenguaje

A continuación encontrará un pequeño poema que
usted y su hijo pueden aprender en inglés y en
español.

Hello!
Hello, hello!
Hello, and
  How are you?
I'm fine,
I'm fine,
And I hope that
  you are, too!

¡Hola!
¡Hola, hola!
Hola y
  ¿cómo estás?
Estoy bien,
estoy bien,
y ¡espero que
  estés bien, también!

La hora del español

A continuación encontrará una canción que puede
cantar con su hijo. Cántela con la melodía de "Frére
Jacques."

Buenos días, buenos días,
¿cómo estás? ¿cómo estás?
Muy bien, gracias,
muy bien, gracias,
¿y usted? ¿y usted?

Buenas noches, buenas noches,
¿cómo estás? ¿cómo estás?
Muy bien, gracias,
muy bien, gracias,
¿y usted? ¿y usted?

School-Home Link
Newsletter 2

Some New Words We've Learned

Action Words

Your child has been learning words that name actions:

- standing
- sitting
- sleeping
- jumping

Other Words

Here are some other words your child has learned:

- pencil
- banana
- man
- car
- ruler
- sandwich
- woman
- flag

Activity Update

We played "Roll the Cube!" We rolled the Actions Cube and did the actions. Play this game with your child using the Actions Cube he or she brings home. Here's how to play:

1. The first player rolls the Actions Cube.

2. The player says the action that lands faceup.

3. Perform the action with your child.

4. Take turns rolling the Actions Cube.

5. Continue playing until all actions have been done.

Things to Talk About at Home

Your Child's Last Name

Your child has been learning to say his or her whole name—first and last name. Have your child practice saying, "My name is _____ _____."

Picture books

Look at picture books with your child. Talk about the different actions that you see. Have your child tell you what the animals and people are doing. For example: Are they sitting down? Are they standing up?

Family Pictures

Look at family photos with your child. Talk about your family members. Talk about who the people are and what their names are. Ask your child to say the first name and then the whole name.

Language Fun

Here's a little action game you and your child can play. Follow the actions in each line.

Hands on Shoulders

Hands on shoulders,

Hands on knees,

Hands behind you,

If you please;

Touch your shoulders,

Now your nose,

Now your hair, and

Now your toes.

Conexión con la escuela y la casa
Boletín 2

Algunas palabras que hemos aprendido

Palabras de acción

Su hijo ha aprendido palabras que significan acciones:

- standing
- sitting
- sleeping
- jumping

Otras palabras

Éstas son otras palabras que su hijo ha aprendido:

- pencil
- banana
- man
- car
- ruler
- sandwich
- woman
- flag

Actividades de última hora

Jugamos "¡Lanza el cubo!" Lanzamos los Cubos de acción e hicimos las acciones. Juegue este juego con su hijo usando los Cubos de acción que él o ella lleve a la casa. Así es como se juega:

1. El primer jugador lanza los Cubos de acción.

2. El jugador dice la acción que queda boca arriba.

3. Haga la acción con su hijo.

4. Túrnense lanzando los Cubos de acción.

5. Siga jugando hasta que se hagan todas las acciones.

Cosas sobre qué conversar en el hogar

El apellido de su hijo

Su hijo ha aprendido a decir su nombre completo— nombre y apellido. Pídale que practique diciendo, "Mi nombre es ____ ____."

Libros de ilustraciones

Vea libros con ilustraciones con su hijo. Hable sobre las diferentes acciones que observa. Pida a su hijo que le diga qué están haciendo los animales y las personas. Por ejemplo: ¿Ellos están sentados? ¿Ellos están parados?

Fotografías de la familia

Observe las fotos familiares con su hijo. Hable sobre los familiares. Hable sobre quiénes son y cuáles son sus nombres. Pida a su hijo que diga el primer nombre y luego el nombre completo.

Diviértete con el lenguaje

A continuación encontrará un pequeño juego de acción que usted y su hijo pueden jugar. Siga las acciones de cada una de las líneas.

Hands on Shoulders

Hands on shoulders,

Hands on knees,

Hands behind you,

If you please;

Touch your shoulders,

Now your nose,

Now your hair, and

Now your toes.

School-Home Link
Newsletter 3

Some New Words We've Learned

Animals

Your child has been learning names of animals:

- cat
- dog
- horse
- monkey

Other Words

Here are some other words your child has learned:

- window
- bus
- house
- bike
- cabinet
- clock
- bookcase
- shirt
- door
- crayon

Activity Update

We played "Road Race!" You can play this game with your child on the game board your child brought home. Here's how to play:

1. Each player chooses a car and puts it on the "start" arrow.

2. The first player tosses a penny or button onto the circle.

3. That player moves one or two spaces.

4. The player must name the object the car stops on and say, "This is a ____."

5. Players take turns tossing the penny and moving their car.

6. The first player to cross the finish line is the winner.

Things to Talk About at Home

Names

Here are some basic facts your child needs to know. Ask your child to tell you:

1. His or her whole name (first and last)

2. Name of the teacher

3. Name of the school

Reading Time

Read a book to your child. During the story, point to the pictures and ask your child to name the objects. Take time to enjoy and discuss the pictures.

Follow the Leader

Here is a little game you can play with your child. Make up a pattern of clapping your hands and tapping your feet (for example: *clap, clap, tap, tap*). Ask your child to repeat the pattern. This will help your child develop the skill of repeating patterns and sounds. Make the pattern longer as your child gets better at the game.

Language Fun

Here's a little action rhyme you can do with your child.

Teddy Bear, Teddy Bear
Teddy bear, teddy bear, turn around.
(turn around)
Teddy bear, teddy bear, touch the ground.
(touch the ground)
Teddy bear, teddy bear, how do you do?
(shake hands)
Teddy bear, teddy bear, I love you!
(hug yourself or each other)

Conexión con la escuela y la casa
Boletín 3

Algunas palabras que hemos aprendido

Animales
Su hijo ha aprendido nombres de animales.

- cat
- horse
- dog
- monkey

Otras palabras
Éstas son otras palabras que su hijo ha aprendido:

- window
- house
- cabinet
- bookcase
- door
- bus
- bike
- clock
- shirt
- crayon

Actividades de última hora

Jugamos "¡La carrera!" Usted puede jugar este juego con su hijo en el tablero de juegos que su hijo llevó para la casa. Así es como se juega:

1. Cada jugador elige un carro y lo coloca en la línea de "salida".

2. El primer jugador lanza un *penny* o un botón dentro del círculo.

3. Ese jugador se mueve uno o dos espacios.

4. El jugador debe nombrar el objeto donde se detuvo el carro y decir, "Esto es un(a) _____."

5. Los jugadores se turnan para lanzar el *penny* y mover sus carros.

6. El primer jugador en cruzar la meta es el ganador.

Cosas sobre qué conversar en el hogar

Nombres
A continuación encontrará algunas cosas básicas que su hijo necesita saber. Pida a su hijo que le diga:

1. Su nombre completo (primer nombre y apellido)

2. El nombre del maestro

3. El nombre de la escuela

Momento de lectura
Léale un libro a su hijo. Durante el cuento, señale las ilustraciones y pida a su hijo que nombre los objetos. Disfrute y comente las ilustraciones.

Sigue al líder
A continuación encontrará un pequeño juego que puede jugar con su hijo. Siga un modelo de aplaudir o de zapatear (por ejemplo: *clap, clap, tap, tap*). Pida a su hijo que lo haga de la misma manera. Esto ayudará a su hijo a desarrollar las destrezas de repetir patrones y sonidos. Alargue el patrón de aplaudir y zapatear para que su hijo realice mejor el juego.

Diviértete con el lenguaje

A continuación encontrará una pequeña rima de acción que puede hacer con su hijo.

Teddy Bear, Teddy Bear
Teddy bear, teddy bear, turn around.
(turn around)
Teddy bear, teddy bear, touch the ground.
(touch the ground)
Teddy bear, teddy bear, how do you do?
(shake hands)
Teddy bear, teddy bear, I love you!
(hug yourself or each other)

School-Home Link
Newsletter 4

Some New Words We've Learned

Toys

Your child has been learning words that name toys:

- wagon
- ball
- bike

Other Words

Here are some other words your child has learned:

- box
- wall
- deer
- glass
- floor
- turtle

Activity Update

We made a picture of a bus and put people on it. The words your child should practice are: *boy, girl, woman, man.* Have your child tell you what person is in each bus window by saying, "This is a ___."

Guess What I Want to Say!

You can help your child tell about actions in complete sentences. Here's what to do:

1. "Let's pretend that I can't talk. I will show you what I want to say."

2. Show your child actions such as brushing your teeth, combing your hair, or sweeping the floor.

3. Ask your child to tell you what you are doing in a complete sentence. For example: "I am brushing my teeth."

4. Continue with more actions. Take turns with your child!

Things to Talk About at Home

Making Introductions with Whole Names

Pretend that toys or stuffed animals are family members. Introduce them to each other using whole names. For example: "María Gonzales, this is Rosa Gonzales."

Picture Books

Read a book to your child. During the story, look for pictures of a girl, a boy, a woman, and a man. Then ask your child to identify what the people are doing.

TV Time

While watching television with your child, talk about the characters. What are their names? What are they doing? What might happen next?

Language Fun

Here's a rhyme you can do with your child.

One, two
How do you do?
(Shake hands with each other.)
One, two, three
Clap with me.
(Clap hands 3 times.)
One, two, three, four
Jump on the floor.
(Jump up and down 4 times.)
One, two, three, four, five
See the bees in the hive.
(Make your fingers on one hand fly around and land in the hive made with the other hand.)

Conexión con la escuela y la casa
Boletín 4

Algunas palabras que hemos aprendido

Juguetes
Su hijo ha aprendido palabras que nombran juguetes:

- wagon
- ball
- bike

Otras palabras
Éstas son otras palabras que su hijo ha aprendido:

- box
- wall
- deer
- glass
- floor
- turtle

Actividades de última hora

Hicimos una ilustración de un autobús y colocamos personas adentro. Las palabras que su hijo deberá practicar son: *boy, girl, woman, man.* Pida a su hijo que le diga qué persona se encuentra en cada una de las ventanas del autobús diciendo, "Éste es un(a) _____."

¡Adivina lo que quiero decir!

Usted puede ayudar a su hijo a decir las acciones y completar las oraciones. Esto es lo que hay que hacer:

1. "Imaginemos que no puedo hablarte. Te enseñaré qué quiero decir."

2. Muestre a su hijo acciones como cepillarse los dientes, peinarse o barrer el piso.

3. Pida a su hijo que le diga qué está haciendo usted en una oración completa. Por ejemplo: "Me estoy cepillando los dientes."

4. Continúe con más acciones. ¡Túrnese con su hijo!

Cosas sobre qué conversar en el hogar

Hacer presentaciones con nombres completos
Imagínense que los juguetes o los animales de peluche son familiares. Preséntelos entre sí usando nombres completos. Por ejemplo: "María González, ésta es Rosa González."

Libros de ilustraciones
Léale un libro a su hijo. Durante el cuento, busque ilustraciones de una niña, un niño, una mujer y un hombre. Luego, pida a su hijo que identifique qué están haciendo las personas.

Hora de ver la televisión
Mientras está viendo la televisión con su hijo, hable sobre los personajes. ¿Cuáles son sus nombres? ¿Que están haciendo? ¿Qué podría pasar después?

Diviértete con el lenguaje

A continuación encontrará una rima que puede hacer con su hijo.

One, two
How do you do?
(Shake hands with each other.)
One, two, three
Clap with me.
(Clap hands 3 times.)
One, two, three, four
Jump on the floor.
(Jump up and down 4 times.)
One, two, three, four, five
See the bees in the hive.
(Make your fingers on one hand fly around and land in the hive made with the other hand.)

School-Home Link
Newsletter 5

Some New Words We've Learned

More Animals

Your child has learned the names of some more animals:

- bird
- cow
- elephant

Other Words

Here are some other words your child has learned:

- egg
- chalk
- ear
- nose
- kite
- balloon
- jar
- head

Activity Update

Your child made a picture of a barn with doors that open. Ask your child to open the doors and "Say the whole thing" about what is inside. For example: "This is a cat."

Old MacDonald Had a Farm

Use the barn picture your child made. Open one door as you sing each verse of the song.

*Old MacDonald had a farm,
E-I-E-I-O.
And on his farm he had a (bird, cat, horse, cow, tree), E-I-E-I-O.
With a __ __ here, and a __ __ there, ...*

Sounds to use:

bird *chirp, chirp*   cow *moo, moo*

cat *meow, meow*   tree *tree, tree*

horse *neigh, neigh*

Things to Talk About at Home

Whole Names

Check to see if your child knows *your* first and whole name. Have your child practice making an introduction. For example: "Mrs. Thomas, this is my mother, Marta López." Do more introductions with names of other family members.

What Will Happen Next?

Begin reading or telling a story. Stop at an exciting point, and ask your child to guess what will happen next. Continue the story and see if the guess was correct. Stop and have your child guess several times during the story. This will help your child build reading comprehension skills.

Guess Who?

Find a picture of three or more people in a book or magazine. Give your child three clues about one person in the picture. For example: "The person is not tall, has a blue shirt, and does not have a hat." Your child can guess which person. Take turns playing "Guess Who?"

Guess-a-Part Game

Here's a game to help your child learn to identify parts of the body.

Give your child a short description about what a part does and let the child finish the sentence. Here are some examples:

You see with your ____.
You hear with your ____.
You put your hat on your ____.
You clap with your ____.

Conexión con la escuela y la casa
Boletín 5

Algunas palabras que hemos aprendido

Más animales
Su hijo aprendió los nombres de otros animales:

- bird
- cow
- elephant

Otras palabras
Éstas son otras palabras que su hijo ha aprendido:

- egg
- chalk
- ear
- nose
- kite
- balloon
- jar
- head

Actividades de última hora
Su hijo dibujó un granero con puertas que se abren. Pida a su hijo que abra las puertas y "Diga toda la oración" de lo que está adentro. Por ejemplo: "Éste es un gato."

El viejo MacDonald tenía una granja
Use el granero que su hijo dibujó. Abra una puerta a medida que canta cada verso de la canción.

Old MacDonald had a farm,
E-I-E-I-O.
And on his farm he had a (bird, cat, horse, cow,
  tree), E-I-E-I-O.
With a __ __ here, and a __ __ there, ...

Sonidos que puede usar:
bird *chirp, chirp*   cow *moo, moo*
cat *meow, meow*   tree *tree, tree*
horse *neigh, neigh*

Cosas sobre qué conversar en el hogar

Nombres completos
Verifique para saber si su hijo sabe su nombre completo. Pida a su hijo que practique haciendo una presentación. Por ejemplo: "Sra. Thomas, ésta es mi mamá, Marta López." Realice más presentaciones con los nombres de otros familiares.

¿Qué sucederá después?
Comience leyendo o contando un cuento. Deténgase en un momento interesante y pida a su hijo que adivine qué pasará después. Continúe con el cuento y vea si la adivinanza fue correcta. Deténgase y pídale a su hijo que adivine varias veces durante el cuento. Esto ayudará a su hijo a formar las destrezas de la comprensión de lectura.

¿Adivina quién?
Encuentre en un libro o una revista una ilustración de tres o más personas. Dé a su hijo tres claves sobre una persona de la ilustración. Por ejemplo: "La persona no es alta, tiene una camisa azul y no tiene sombrero." Su hijo puede adivinar cuál es la persona. Túrnense para jugar "¿Adivina quién?"

El juego de adivinar una parte
A continuación encontrará un juego para ayudar a su hijo a identificar las partes del cuerpo.

Dé a su hijo una pequeña descripción sobre lo que hace una parte y deje que su hijo termine la oración. Aquí tiene algunos ejemplos:

Tú ves con los ____.
Tú oyes con las ____.
Te pones el sombrero en la ____.
Aplaudes con las ____.

School-Home Link
Newsletter 6

Some New Words We've Learned

Here are some new words your child has learned:

- ceiling
- sink
- telephone
- ducks
- leaf
- mouth
- dollar

Activity Update

Your child has made and laced a pair of paper shoes. Then we played a game matching pairs of shoes together.

If your child doesn't already know, help your child learn to lace and tie shoelaces.

Shoe Sort

Get out four or five pairs of shoes. Have your child sort all of the shoes for the *right* foot into one pile and all the shoes for the *left* foot into another pile.

Shoe Scramble

Take a pair of your child's shoes and mix them behind your back. Give them to your child. See if your child can put them on the correct feet.

Spanish Time

Here's a fun poem about dancing feet.

Con un pie, con un pie,
con un pie yo bailo.
Con un pie, con un pie;
yo bailo con un pie.
Con dos pies, con dos pies,
con dos pies yo bailo.
Con dos pies, con dos pies;
Yo bailo con dos pies.

Things to Talk About at Home

Finding Directions in Pictures

You can help your child understand direction words such as *on* and *over.*

You will need a magazine, catalog, or newspaper ads.

Here's what to do:

1. Look through the pictures in the magazine, catalog, or newspaper ad to find pictures of things that are *on* or *over.* Examples might include: a car *on* the street, carpet *over* the floor, a ring *on* a finger, cloth *over* a table.

2. Discuss with your child why things in the pictures are *on* or *over* something. Talk about what the things are *on* and what the things are *over.*

3. Walk through your house together. Ask your child to find examples of things that are *on* or *over.*

Language Fun

Here's a little song you and your child can sing to the tune of "The Farmer in the Dell."

We all wear shoes,
We all wear shoes,
To keep our feet so warm and clean,
We all wear shoes.

We wear them when we jump,
We wear them when we jump,
To keep our feet so warm and clean,
We wear them when we jump.

(Continue with "when we run," "when it snows," and "when it rains.")

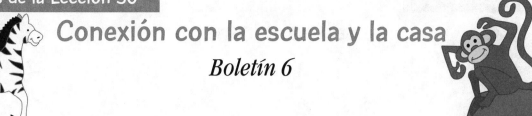

Conexión con la escuela y la casa
Boletín 6

Algunas palabras que hemos aprendido

A continuación encontrará algunas palabras nuevas que su hijo ha aprendido:

- ceiling
- sink
- telephone
- ducks
- leaf
- mouth
- dollar

Actividades de última hora

Su hijo ha hecho y atado un par de zapatos de papel. Después, jugamos un juego donde emparejamos los zapatos.

Si su hijo no sabe hacerlo todavía, ayúdelo a amarrarse los zapatos.

Clasificar zapatos

Busque cuatro o cinco pares de zapatos. Pida a su hijo que clasifique los zapatos del lado *derecho* en una pila y los del lado *izquierdo* en otra.

Revoltijo de zapatos

Tome un par de zapatos de su hijo y mézclelos detrás de su espalda. Déle los zapatos a su hijo. Vea si su hijo puede ponérselos en el pie correcto.

La hora del español

A continuación encontrará un gracioso poema sobre bailes con el pie.

Con un pie, con un pie,
con un pie yo bailo.
Con un pie, con un pie;
yo bailo con un pie.
Con dos pies, con dos pies,
con dos pies yo bailo.
Con dos pies, con dos pies;
yo bailo con dos pies.

Cosas sobre qué conversar en el hogar
Hallar direcciones en las ilustraciones

Usted puede ayudar a su hijo a comprender palabras de dirección como *en, sobre, encima* y *por encima.*

Necesitará una revista, un catálogo o un periódico.

Esto es lo que hay que hacer:

1. Observe las ilustraciones en la revista, el catálogo o el periódico para encontrar ilustraciones de cosas que están *sobre* o *encima.* Los ejemplos podrían incluir: un carro *en* la calle, una alfombra *sobre* el piso, un anillo *en* el dedo, una ropa *encima* de la mesa.

2. Comente con su hijo por qué las cosas en la ilustración se encuentran *en* o *encima* de algo. Hable sobre qué cosas están *en* y qué cosas *están* encima.

3. Caminen por la casa. Pida a su hijo que encuentre ejemplos de cosas que están *en* o *encima.*

Diviértete con el lenguaje

A continuación encontrará una pequeña canción que usted y su hijo pueden cantar con la melodía de "The Farmer in the Dell."

We all wear shoes,
We all wear shoes,
To keep our feet so warm and clean,
We all wear shoes.

We wear them when we jump,
We wear them when we jump,
To keep our feet so warm and clean,
We wear them when we jump.

(Siguen con "when we run," "when it snows," y "when it rains.")

School-Home Link
Newsletter 7

Some New Words We've Learned

Important Direction Words
- on
- over
- in front of

Other Words
- sack
- oars
- boat
- tiger
- toothbrush
- axe
- apple

Activity Update

Your child has been learning to name parts of the body. We played a game called "Spin a Person." Ask your child to tell you about the game. Have your child name the parts of the body on the paper person he or she brought home (head, body, arms, legs).

Yes or No Game

Here's a game you can use to help your child learn important direction words.

1. Put a box on a table.

2. Put toys or kitchen objects *on, in front of,* or *over* the box.

3. Ask your child "yes" or "no" questions about the location of each object. For example, "Is the spoon *in* the box?" "Is the car *in front of* the box?" "Is the towel *over* the box?"

Things to Talk About at Home

What Goes with It?
Play this word game with your child. Say a word and have your child say a word that goes with it. For example:

fork (goes with) knife or spoon
pencil (goes with) paper
night (goes with) day

Parts and Whole
Your child has been learning the parts of a table and a pencil. Show your child a table. Point to the leg. Ask, "What is this part called?" Point to the top. Ask, "What is this part called?" Ask, "What's the whole object called?" Show your child a pencil. Point to the point. Ask, "What is this part called?" Point to the shaft. Ask, "What is this part called?" Point to the eraser. Ask, "What is this part called?" Ask, "What's the whole object called?"

Language Fun

Here's an action poem you can do with your child.

This is the circle that is my head.
(Make a large circle with both hands.)
This is my mouth with which words are said.
(Point to mouth.)
These are my eyes with which I see.
(Point to eyes.)
This is my nose that's a part of me.
(Point to nose.)
This is the hair that grows on my head.
(Point to hair.)
And this is my hat all round and red.
(Place hands on head, fingers pointing up and touching.)

Conexión con la escuela y la casa
Boletín 7

Algunas palabras que hemos aprendido

Palabras importantes de dirección

- on
- over
- in front of

Otras palabras

- sack
- oars
- boat
- tiger
- toothbrush
- axe
- apple

Actividades de última hora

Su hijo ha aprendido a nombrar las partes del cuerpo. Jugamos un juego que se llama "Haz girar a una persona". Pida a su hijo que le hable sobre el juego. Pídale que nombre las partes del cuerpo en el papel de la persona que él o ella lleve a la casa (cabeza, cuerpo, brazos, piernas).

El juego del sí o el no

A continuación encontrará un juego que puede usar para ayudar a su hijo a que comprenda la importancia de las palabras de instrucción.

1. Coloque una caja en una mesa.

2. Coloque juguetes u objetos de cocina *en, en frente de* o *encima de* la caja.

3. Haga preguntas de "sí" o "no" sobre la ubicación de cada uno de los objetos. Por ejemplo: "¿La cuchara está *en* la caja?" "¿El carro está *en frente* de la caja?" "¿La toalla está *encima* de la caja?"

Cosas sobre qué conversar en el hogar

¿Qué va con esto?

Juegue con su hijo este juego de palabras. Diga una palabra y pida a su hijo que diga una palabra que vaya con esa. Por ejemplo:

tenedor (va con) cuchillo o cuchara
lápiz (va con) papel
noche (va con) día

Partes y todo

Su hijo ha aprendido las partes de una mesa y un lápiz. Muéstrele una mesa a su hijo. Señale la pata. Pregunte: "¿Cómo se llama esta parte?" Señale la parte superior de la mesa. Pregunte: "¿Cómo se llama esta parte?" Pregunte: "¿Cómo se llama todo el objeto?" Muestre a su hijo un lápiz. Señale la punta del lápiz. Pregunte: "¿Cómo se llama esta parte?" Señale el borrador. Pregunte: ¿Cómo se llama esta parte?" Pregunte: "¿Cómo se llama todo el objeto?"

Diviértete con el lenguaje

A continuación encontrará un poema de instrucción que puede hacer con su hijo.

This is the circle that is my head.
(Haga un círculo grande con las manos.)
This is my mouth with which words are said.
(Señale la boca.)
These are my eyes with which I see.
(Señale los ojos.)
This is my nose that's a part of me.
(Señale la nariz.)
This is the hair that grows on my head.
(Señale el cabello.)
And this is my hat all round and red.
(Coloque las manos sobre la cabeza, los dedos señalando hacia arriba y tocándose.)

School-Home Link
Newsletter 8

Some New Words We've Learned

Opposites
- big—not big
- top—bottom

Other Words
- giraffe
- motorcycle
- ship
- fence
- bear
- stove
- couch
- dishes

Activity Update

Your child made a paper person that could walk or run. Ask your child to show you these two actions with the paper person.

On or Over?

Cut out the giraffe finger puppet, tape the tabs together, and take turns putting the giraffe *on* or *over* different things in your house. Say, "Where is the giraffe now?" Encourage your child to say, for example: "The giraffe is *on* the couch."

Things to Talk About at Home

Days of the Week
Your child is learning to say the days of the week. Help your child practice at home. Say the name of one day, and have your child say the next day. For example: you say, "Monday," and your child says, "Tuesday." Practice in different ways—with a slow voice, a fast voice, quietly, and loudly.

Tell a Story
When you reread a favorite story, it helps your child learn to remember story sequence. Choose one of your child's favorite books. Read the story to your child. Talk about the events and the characters. When finished, give the book to your child. Have your child "read" the book to you by telling as much as he or she can remember while turning the pages and looking at the pictures.

Make a Book
Fold a piece of paper into three parts. Have your child draw a picture of what happened first, next, and last in the story you just read together.

Language Fun

Here's a poem you can teach your child.

> The fish lives in the brook.
> The bird lives in the tree.
> But home's the very nicest place
> For a young child like me!

Conexión con la escuela y la casa
Boletín 8

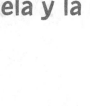

Algunas palabras que hemos aprendido

Opuestos
- big—not big
- top—bottom

Otras palabras
- giraffe
- motorcycle
- ship
- fence
- bear
- stove
- couch
- dishes

Actividades de última hora

Su hijo hizo una persona de papel que podía caminar o correr. Pida a su hijo que le muestre estas dos acciones con la persona de papel.

¿En o encima?

Recorte del títere en forma de jirafa, pegue las etiquetas y túrnense colocando la jirafa *en* o *encima* de diferentes cosas en la casa. Diga: "¿Dónde está la jirafa ahora?" Anime a su hijo a que diga, por ejemplo: "La jirafa está *en* el sofá".

Cosas sobre qué conversar en el hogar

Los días de la semana

Su hijo está aprendiendo a decir los días de la semana. Ayude a su hijo a practicar en la casa. Diga el nombre de un día y pida a su hijo que diga el nombre del día siguiente. Por ejemplo: usted dice— "lunes" y su hijo dice "martes". Practique de maneras diferentes—con voz lenta, voz rápida, en silencio y en voz alta.

Contar un cuento

Cuando vuelve a leer un cuento favorito, ayuda a su hijo a aprender a recordar la secuencia del cuento. Elija uno de los libros favoritos de su hijo. Lea el cuento a su hijo. Hable sobre los sucesos y los personajes. Cuando termine, dé el libro a su hijo. Pida a su hijo que le "lea" el libro diciendo tanto como él o ella pueda recordar mientras voltea las páginas y observa las ilustraciones.

Hacer un libro

Doble una hoja de papel en tres partes. Pida a su hijo que haga un dibujo de lo que pasó primero, después y de último en el cuento que acaban de leer.

Diviértete con el lenguaje

A continuación encontrará un poema que le puede enseñar a su hijo.

> The fish lives in the brook.
> The bird lives in the tree.
> But home's the very nicest place
> For a young child like me!

School-Home Link
Newsletter 9

Some New Words We've Learned

Opposites
- full—empty
- big—small
- wet—dry

Other Words
- frog
- bowl
- wastebasket
- owl

Activity Update

We played a game called "Build an Elephant." Your child put together an elephant using *a body, legs, trunk,* and *tail.* Ask your child to tell you the parts of an elephant.

Language Fun

Teach your child this action poem.

The Elephant

The elephant has a trunk for a nose,

And up and down is the way it goes.

(Clasp hands together, extend arms, and raise them.)

He wears such a saggy, baggy, hide! *(Relax body.)*

Do you think two elephants would fit inside? *(Hold up two fingers.)*

Plurals Practice

Teach your child "Head, Shoulders, Knees and Toes" with the actions.

Head, shoulders, knees and toes, knees and toes.
Head, shoulders, knees and toes, knees and toes.
And eyes and ears and mouth and nose.
Head, shoulders, knees and toes, knees and toes.

Things to Talk About at Home

Days of the Week

Help your child practice saying the days of the week. Each day when your child gets up, talk about what day of the week it is and what you do on that day. Ask your child to say the days of the week, starting with Sunday.

Copy Cat Game

Help your child listen to and remember word patterns. Here's what to do:

1. Say three words to your child that are in the same class (food, clothing, toys, furniture).

2. Ask your child to repeat the words in the same order. Here are some examples of patterns:

   table, chair, bookcase

   hat, shoes, shirt

   banana, sandwich, carrots

3. Add on words as your child gets better at this game.

4. Let your child play the game with you!

Memory Tray

Place three or four small kitchen items on a cookie sheet or place mat. Cover them with a towel. Take off the towel and let your child look at the items for a few moments. Put the towel back on. Ask your child not to peek while you remove one item. Take off the towel and ask your child, "What did I take away?" After your child gets good at the game, try taking away two items and adding more items to the tray.

Conexión con la escuela y la casa
Boletín 9

Algunas palabras que hemos aprendido

Opuestos
- full—empty
- big—small
- wet—dry

Otras palabras
- frog
- wastebasket
- bowl
- owl

Actividades de última hora

Jugamos un juego llamado "Hacer un elefante". Su hijo armó un elefante usando un cuerpo, unas patas, una trompa y una cola. Pida a su hijo que le diga las partes de un elefante.

Diviértete con el lenguaje

Enseñe a su hijo este poema de acción.

The Elephant

The elephant has a trunk for a nose,

And up and down is the way it goes.

(Aplaudan juntos, extiendan los brazos y levántenlos.)

He wears such a saggy, baggy, hide! *(Relajen el cuerpo.)*

Do *you* think two elephants would fit inside? *(Levanten dos dedos.)*

Practicar plurales

Enseñe a su hijo "Cabeza, hombros, rodillas y dedos de los pies" con acciones.

Head, shoulders, knees and toes, knees and toes.
Head, shoulders, knees and toes, knees and toes.
And eyes and ears and mouth and nose.
Head, shoulders, knees and toes, knees and toes.

Cosas sobre qué conversar en el hogar

Los días de la semana

Ayude a su hijo a practicar diciendo los días de la semana. Cuando su hijo se levante todos los días, hable sobre qué día de la semana es ese y qué hace usted ese día. Pida a su hijo que diga los días de la semana, comenzando con domingo.

El juego de copiar

Ayude a su hijo a escuchar y a recordar patrones de palabras. Esto es lo que hay que hacer:

1. Diga tres palabras a su hijo que se encuentren en la misma clase (comida, ropa, juguetes, muebles).

2. Pida a su hijo que repita las palabras en el mismo orden. Éstos son algunos ejemplos de patrones:

   mesa, silla, biblioteca

   sombrero, zapatos, camisa

   banana, sándwich, zanahorias

3. Agregue palabras a medida que su hijo mejora en este juego.

4. ¡Deje que su hijo juegue el juego con usted!

Bandeja de memoria

Coloque tres o cuatro artículos de cocina pequeños en una bandeja de galletas o en una alfombra. Cúbralas con una toalla. Quite la toalla y deje que su hijo observe los artículos por unos momentos. Coloque la toalla nuevamente. Pida a su hijo que no haga trampas mientras usted quita uno de los artículos. Quite la toalla y pregunte a su hijo, "¿Qué fue lo que quite?" Después de que su hijo mejore en el juego, pruebe quitando dos artículos y agregando más artículos a la bandeja.

School-Home Link
Newsletter 10

Some New Words We've Learned

Pronouns
- she
- he
- they
- her
- his

Other Words
- pot
- rabbit
- stool
- worm

Activity Update

We made a bear hat. Ask your child to point out the head, ears, eyes, and nose of the bear.

What's in the Bag?

Put a common object such as a spoon, cup, or salt shaker into a paper bag. Ask your child to reach into the bag, feel the object, describe it, and guess what it is without looking.

Kitchen Words

Help your child learn these kitchen words by filling in a word that best fits the sentence.

1. With a spoon, I eat my ___. (food)

2. On the stove I cook ___. (food, dinner)

3. I turn on the faucet to get ___. (water)

4. I put my plate on the ___. (table)

5. I cut my food with a ___. (knife)

Things to Talk About at Home

Calendar Talk

Ask your child what day of the week it is. Talk about what things you do on this day of the week. Talk about what things you do on other days of the week. For example: "We go to the grocery store on Saturday."

Telephone Number

Help your child learn your telephone number. Practice the first three numbers, then teach the next four numbers. When your child can say both sets of numbers, put them together.

Language Fun

Little Wiggle Worm Fingerplay

Teach your child this fingerplay and sing it to the tune of "The Itsy Bitsy Spider."

> The little wiggle worm went crawling
>   underground.
> *(Make your finger crawl up and down.)*
> Down came the rain, soon mud was all around.
> *(Make your fingers show rain coming down.)*
> Rain filled up the tunnels and pushed out little
>   worm.
> *(Make a pushing away motion with your hands
>   together.)*
> So the puddles on the ground
> *(Move hands in circling motions.)*
> were the only place to squirm.
> *(Put both palms up and give your shoulders a
>   shrug.)*

Conexión con la escuela y la casa
Boletín 10

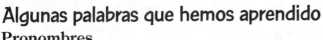

Algunas palabras que hemos aprendido

Pronombres
- she
- he
- they
- her
- his

Otras palabras
- pot
- rabbit
- stool
- worm

Actividades de última hora

Hicimos un sombrero de oso. Pida a su hijo que señale la cabeza, los oídos, los ojos y la nariz del oso.

¿Qué hay en la bolsa?

Coloque un objeto común y corriente como una cuchara, un vaso o un salero en una bolsa de papel. Pida a su hijo que busque dentro de la bolsa, que toque el objeto, que lo describa y que adivine qué es sin mirar.

Palabras de cocina

Ayude a su hijo a que aprenda estas palabras de cocina al colocar la palabra que complete mejor la oración.

1. Con una cuchara como mi ___. (comida)

2. En la cocina yo cocino la ___. (comida, cena)

3. Yo abro el grifo para que salga el ___. (agua)

4. Yo coloco mi plato sobre la ___. (mesa)

5. Yo corto mis alimentos con un ____. (cuchillo)

Cosas sobre qué conversar en el hogar

Hablar del calendario

Pregunte a su hijo qué día de la semana es. Hable sobre las cosas que usted hace durante ese día de la semana. Por ejemplo: "Los sábados vamos a la tienda."

Número telefónico

Ayude a su hijo a que aprenda su número telefónico. Practique los tres primeros números, luego enséñele los cuatro números que siguen. Una los números cuando su hijo pueda decir ambos grupos de números.

Diviértete con el lenguaje

El juego de dedos de la pequeña lombriz Wiggle

Enseñe a su hijo este juego de dedos y cántelo al compás de la música de "La araña pequeñita."

The little wiggle worm went crawling underground.
(Haga que sus dedos suban y bajen.)
Down came the rain, soon mud was all around.
(Haga que sus dedos muestren la lluvia que cae.)
Rain filled up the tunnels and pushed out little worm.
(Haga como si empuje con sus manos juntas.)
So the puddles on the ground
(Mueva sus manos con movimientos circulares.)
were the only place to squirm.
(Coloque las palmas hacia arriba y encoja los hombros.)

School-Home Link
Newsletter 11

Some New Words We've Learned

Vehicles
- truck
- train
- airplane
- boat

Order Words
- first
- next
- last

Other Words
- ribbon
- cake
- stick
- paper
- cage
- bone
- pig

Activity Update

We made a "Short to Long Doggie." Have your child show you how the doggie can "grow" from short to long. Use the words *first* and *next* to describe what the doggie does. For example: "First the doggie is short, next the doggie is long."

More Short to Long

Cut straws or long spaghetti into pieces of different lengths. Ask your child to arrange the pieces in a row from shortest to longest.

Make Your Own Puzzle

Help your child make a puzzle. Cut a picture from a greeting card, calendar, or magazine cover into large pieces. Have your child put the picture back together on a sheet of paper.

Things to Talk About at Home

Telephone Number

After your child can say your telephone number, have your child practice dialing the number on the telephone.

Vehicles

We have been talking about vehicles. Help your child learn more about vehicles. Here's what to do:

1. Look in magazines for pictures of trucks, trains, cars, boats, and airplanes. Help your child cut them out.

2. Lay the pictures on the table. Ask your child questions about the vehicles.
   - What goes through the air?
   - What runs on tracks?
   - What goes in the water?
   - What carries big loads?
   - What do most people drive?

3. Ask your child to point to the correct vehicle and identify it.

Language Fun

Dog Songs

Have fun singing some dog songs with your child. For example:

"Where, Oh Where Has My Little Dog Gone?"
"Bingo"
"How Much Is That Doggie in the Window?"

Conexión con la escuela y la casa
Boletín 11

Algunas palabras que hemos aprendido

Vehículos
- truck
- airplane
- train
- boat

Palabras para ordenar
- first
- next
- last

Otras palabras
- ribbon
- cage
- cake
- bone
- stick
- pig
- paper

Actividades de última hora

Hicimos un "Perrito que se hizo grande". Pida a su hijo que muestre cómo el perro puede "crecer" de pequeño a grande. Use las palabras *primero* y *luego* para describir al perro. Por ejemplo: "Primero el perro es pequeño, luego es grande".

Más sobre pequeño a grande

Recorte pajitas o espaguetis grandes en pedazos de longitudes diferentes. Pida a su hijo que clasifique las piezas en una fila desde el más pequeño hasta el más grande.

Haz tu propio rompecabezas

Ayude a su hijo a realizar un rompecabezas. Recorte una ilustración de una tarjeta de felicitaciones, un calendario o la portada de una revista en pedazos grandes. Pida a su hijo que una la ilustración en una hoja de papel.

Cosas sobre qué conversar en el hogar

Número telefónico

Después que su hijo pueda decir su número telefónico, pídale que practique marcando el número en el teléfono.

Vehículos

Hemos hablado sobre los vehículos. Ayude a su hijo a que aprenda más sobre los vehículos. Esto es lo que hay que hacer:

1. Busque en las revistas ilustraciones de camiones, trenes, carros, botes y aviones. Ayude a su hijo a recortarlos.

2. Coloque las ilustraciones en la mesa. Pregúntele a su hijo sobre las ilustraciones.

   - ¿Qué va por el aire?
   - ¿Qué rueda sobre rieles?
   - ¿Qué va sobre el agua?
   - ¿Qué lleva grandes cargamentos?
   - ¿Qué es lo que la mayoría de las personas conduce?

3. Pida a su hijo que señale el vehículo correcto y lo identifique.

Diviértete con el lenguaje

Canciones sobre perros

Diviértase con su hijo cantando algunas canciones sobre perros. Por ejemplo:

"Where, Oh Where Has My Little Dog Gone?"

"Bingo"

"How Much Is That Doggie in the Window?"

School-Home Link
Newsletter 12

Some New Words We've Learned

More Vehicles
- canoe
- taxi
- sailboat
- tricycle
- rowboat

More Opposites
- full—empty
- big—small
- wet—dry
- long—short
- old—young

Other Words
- mouse
- alligator
- umbrella
- coat
- football
- shovel

Activity Update

We made a paper turtle. Have your child show you how the turtle can move his head in, out, up, and down.

Language Fun

My Turtle Action Poem

Ask your child to use the paper turtle to show the actions as you read the poem.

> This is my little turtle.
> *(Hold the turtle.)*
> He lives in a shell.
> *(Point to the shell.)*
> He likes his home very well.
> *(Pull head in. Nod head.)*
> He pokes his head out
> *(Push head out.)*
> When he wants to eat.
> *(Push head down.)*
> And he pulls it back
> *(Pull head in.)*
> When he wants to sleep.
> *(Child closes eyes and "sleeps.")*

Things to Talk About at Home

Emergencies

Discuss with your child what to do in an emergency. Decide what telephone number your child should call, and teach your child that number and how to dial it.

Looking for Opposites

Read a story to your child that has lots of pictures. As you read, talk about opposites you see in the story: wet—dry, long—short, big—small, old—young.

Sorting Big and Small

Find pictures in catalogs or magazines of things that are big and small. Cut out the pictures. Ask your child to sort the pictures into two piles: big and small. Ask your child to tell you why some pictures were put in the "big pile," and some pictures were put in the "small pile."

Going Places

Here's a vehicles game you can play with your child. Say, "I'll name a place we can go and you tell me how to get there—by bike, car, plane, or boat."

Give your child the names of familiar places, such as: grocery store, a friend's house, the school, and so on. You can also say the names of other countries or areas across a body of water for air or boat travel.

Conexión con la escuela y la casa
Boletín 12

Algunas palabras que hemos aprendido

Más vehículos
- canoe
- sailboat
- rowboat
- taxi
- tricycle

Más opuestos
- full—empty
- wet—dry
- old—young
- big—small
- long—short

Otras palabras
- mouse
- umbrella
- football
- alligator
- coat
- shovel

Actividades de última hora

Hicimos una tortuga de papel. Pida a su hijo que le muestre cómo la tortuga puede mover su cabeza hacia dentro, hacia afuera, hacia arriba y hacia abajo.

Diviértete con el lenguaje

Mi poema de acción de la tortuga

Pida a su hijo que use la tortuga de papel para mostrar las acciones a medida que usted lee el poema.

> This is my little turtle.
> *(Sostenga la tortuga.)*
> He lives in a shell.
> *(Señale la cáscara.)*
> He likes his home very well.
> *(Meta la cabeza. Incline la cabeza.)*
> He pokes his head out
> *(Empuje la cabeza hacia afuera.)*
> When he wants to eat.
> *(Empuje la cabeza hacia abajo.)*
> And he pulls it back
> *(Meta la cabeza.)*
> When he wants to sleep.
> *(El niño cierra los ojos y "duerme.")*

Cosas sobre qué conversar en el hogar

Emergencias

Comente con su hijo qué hacer en una emergencia. Decida a qué número de teléfono su hijo podría llamar y enséñele ese número y cómo marcarlo.

Buscando los opuestos

Lea una historia a su hijo que tenga muchas ilustraciones. A medida que lee, hable sobre los opuestos que ve en la historia: mojado—seco, largo—corto, grande—pequeño, viejo—joven.

Clasificar en grandes y pequeños

Busque ilustraciones en catálogos o revistas de cosas que sean grandes y pequeñas. Recorte las ilustraciones. Pida a su hijo que clasifique las ilustraciones en dos pilas: grandes y pequeñas. Pida a su hijo que le diga por qué algunas ilustraciones fueron puestas en la "pila grande" y otras en la "pila pequeña."

Ir a lugares

A continuación encontrará un juego de vehículos el cual puede jugar con su hijo. Diga, "Nombraré un lugar al cual podemos ir y tú me dirás cómo podemos ir allá, en bicicleta, en carro, en avión o en bote."

Dé a su hijo los nombres de lugares familiares como: la tienda de alimentos, la casa de un amigo, la escuela y así sucesivamente. También puede mencionar los nombres de otros países o áreas donde se viaje por aire o por barco.

School-Home Link
Newsletter 13

Some New Words We've Learned

Food
- bread
- lettuce
- orange
- potato
- carrot
- cheese
- cookie
- tomato

Other Words
- bucket
- swing
- ant
- ladder
- rope
- plates

Activity Update

We made an "Animal Flip Book." Your child is learning colors and names of animals. Read the following poem as your child turns the pages of the flip book and shows you the colors and animals. Next, see if your child can say the poem with you as you look at the book together.

Brown bear, brown bear,
What do you see?
I see a green frog looking at me.
Green frog, green frog,
What do you see?
I see a yellow rabbit looking at me.
Yellow rabbit, yellow rabbit,
What do you see?
I see a red bird looking at me.
Red bird, red bird,
What do you see?
I see (your child's name) looking at me!

Things to Talk About at Home

Today and Tomorrow

Talk about what day it is today. Say, "Today is ___, so what day will tomorrow be?" Talk about activities your child did today. Then ask your child to draw a picture of an activity that will happen tomorrow and tell you about it.

Direction Words

Help your child learn to use direction words by playing an "I spy" game. Use the words *top, middle, bottom, in, over, in back of, in front of,* and *on.*

1. Tell your child, "I will give you clues about an object in this room. See if you can guess what I spy."

2. For example: say, "I spy, with my little eye, something on the middle shelf."

3. Continue with the game, using more location words.

4. When your child becomes good at the game, see if he or she can give you some clues for guessing.

Language Fun

Engine on the Track Fingerplay

Here is the engine on the track.
(Hold up thumb.)
Here is the coal car, just in back.
(Hold up pointer finger.)
Here is the box car to carry freight.
(Hold up middle finger.)
Here is the mail car. Don't be late!
(Hold up ring finger.)
Way back here at the end of the train,
(Hold up little finger.)
Rides the caboose through the sun and rain.

Conexión con la escuela y la casa
Boletín 13

Algunas palabras que hemos aprendido

Comida

- bread
- lettuce
- orange
- potato

- carrot
- cheese
- cookie
- tomato

Otras palabras

- bucket
- swing
- ant

- ladder
- rope
- plates

Actividades de última hora

Hicimos un "Libro de imágenes de animal." Su hijo está aprendiendo los colores y los nombres de animales. Lea el siguiente poema a medida que su hijo voltea las páginas del libro de imágenes y le muestra los colores y los animales. Después, vea si su hijo puede decir el poema con usted a medida que miran el libro.

Brown bear, brown bear,
What do you see?
I see a green frog looking at me.
Green frog, green frog,
What do you see?
I see a yellow rabbit looking at me.
Yellow rabbit, yellow rabbit,
What do you see?
I see a red bird looking at me.
Red bird, red bird,
What do you see?
I see (el nombre de su hijo) looking at me!

Cosas sobre qué conversar en el hogar

Hoy y mañana

Comente qué día es hoy. Diga, "Hoy es ___, entonces, ¿qué día será mañana?" Hable sobre las actividades que su hijo hizo hoy. Luego, pida a su hijo que dibuje una actividad que sucederá mañana y que hable sobre ella.

Palabras de dirección

Ayude a su hijo a que use palabras de dirección al jugar un juego llamado "Yo veo". Use las palabras *de arriba, medio, de abajo, encima de, atrás de, en frente de* y *sobre*.

1. Diga a su hijo: "Te daré claves sobre los objetos de este cuarto. Ve si puedes adivinar qué veo."

2. Por ejemplo, diga: "Yo veo, con mi ojito, algo en el estante del medio."

3. Continúe con el juego usando más palabras de ubicación.

4. Cuando su hijo mejore en el juego, vea si él o ella puede darle claves para adivinar.

Diviértete con el lenguaje

Juego de dedos del tren en el riel

Here is the engine on the track.
(Levante el pulgar.)
Here is the coal car, just in back.
(Levante el dedo índice.)
Here is the box car to carry freight.
(Levante el dedo medio.)
Here is the mail car. Don't be late!
(Levante el dedo anular.)
Way back here at the end of the train,
(Levante el dedo meñique.)
Rides the caboose through the sun and rain.

School-Home Link
Newsletter 14

Some New Words We've Learned

More Food
- popcorn
- peanut
- meat
- ice cream
- pancakes
- pie

Other Words
- log
- goat
- newspapers
- bed
- comb
- purse
- butterfly
- rug
- basket
- bag
- tablecloth
- squirrel

Activity Update

We played a lotto game with vehicles. Ask your child to show you the lotto card. Have your child identify each of the vehicles on the card.

Play Vehicle Lotto at Home

Put 24 buttons, pennies, or dry beans in a cup to use as markers on the lotto card. Give your child a clue about a vehicle. If your child guesses correctly, he or she can cover that vehicle. Continue playing until all of the vehicles are covered. Here are some example clues:

- It has wings. (plane)
- It is used for farm work. (tractor)

Simon Says

Play "Simon Says" by naming parts of the body. Explain the rules to your child. Say, "I am Simon, and I will tell you what to do. But don't move until you hear the words *Simon says*." Then give your child a command such as, "Simon says, touch your head." Once in a while, leave off "Simon says" to make the game more exciting.

Things to Talk About at Home

Names of Foods

Help your child learn names of foods. Find grocery store ads that picture foods. Have your child cut out pictures of foods he or she is familiar with and some that are not familiar. Then have your child glue the pictures on a piece of paper. Ask your child to name as many of the foods as possible. Then tell your child the names of the foods he or she doesn't know. Keep the pictures and review them until your child knows all of the foods pictured. Add new food pictures as you find them.

If you can eat it, it's food.

Tell your child the rule, "If you can eat it, it's food." Have your child say the rule with you. Then name food and non-food items one at a time. After each item, your child should say, "Food," or "Not food." You can choose words from the "New Words We've Learned" list.

Language Fun

If You're Happy and You Know It

If you're happy and you know it, clap your hands! *(Clap two times.)*
If you're happy and you know it, clap your hands! *(Clap two times.)*
If you're happy and you know it, your face will surely show it.
If you're happy and you know it, clap your hands! *(Clap two times.)*

Second verse: stomp your feet
Third verse: tap your head
Fourth verse: jump up and down

Conexión con la escuela y la casa
Boletín 14

Algunas palabras que hemos aprendido

Más comida
- popcorn
- peanut
- meat
- ice cream
- pancakes
- pie

Otras palabras
- log
- goat
- newspapers
- bed
- comb
- purse
- butterfly
- rug
- basket
- bag
- tablecloth
- squirrel

Actividades de última hora

Jugamos un juego de lotería con vehículos. Pida a su hijo que le muestre la tarjeta de lotería. Pida a su hijo que identifique cada uno de los vehículos en la tarjeta.

Jugar la lotería de vehículos en casa

Coloque 24 botones, pennies o frijoles secos en una taza para usarlos como marcadores en la tarjeta de lotería. Dé a su hijo una clave sobre un vehículo. Si su hijo adivina correctamente, él o ella puede tapar ese vehículo. Continúe jugando hasta que todos los vehículos estén tapados. A continuación encontrará algunas claves de ejemplo:

- Éste tiene alas. (avión)
- Éste se usa para trabajar en las granjas. (tractor)

Simón dice

Juegue "Simón dice" nombrando las partes del cuerpo. Explique las reglas a su hijo. Diga, "Yo soy Simón y te diré qué hacer. Pero no te muevas hasta que oigas las palabras *Simón dice*." Luego dé a su hijo una orden como: "Simón dice, toca tu cabeza." De vez en cuando, omita "Simón dice" para hacer el juego más interesante.

Cosas sobre qué conversar en el hogar

Nombres de alimentos

Ayude a su hijo a que aprenda nombres de alimentos. Encuentre un anuncio de una tienda de alimentos que tenga ilustraciones. Pida a su hijo que recorte las ilustraciones de alimentos con las que él o ella esté familiarizado y las que no esté. Luego, pida a su hijo que pegue las ilustraciones en un pedazo de papel. Pida a su hijo que nombre tantos alimentos como sea posible. Luego, dígale a su hijo los nombres de los alimentos que él o ella no conocen. Guarde las ilustraciones y repáselas hasta que su hijo conozca todos los alimentos ilustrados. Agregue ilustraciones nuevas de alimentos a medida que las encuentre.

Si puedes comerlo, es un alimento

Dígale a su hijo la regla, "Si puedes comerlo, es un alimento." Pida a su hijo que diga la regla con usted. Luego, nombre artículos que sean alimentos y los que no también, uno a la vez. Después de cada artículo, su hijo deberá decir, "Alimento" o "No es un alimento." Usted puede elegir palabras de la lista de "Palabras nuevas que hemos aprendido."

Diviértete con el lenguaje

Si estás feliz y tú lo sabes

If you're happy and you know it, clap your hands! *(Aplaudir dos veces.)*
If you're happy and you know it, clap your hands! *(Aplaudir dos veces.)*
If you're happy and you know it, your face will surely show it.
If you're happy and you know it, clap your hands! *(Aplaudir dos veces.)*

Second verse: stomp your feet
Third verse: tap your head
Fourth verse: jump up and down

School-Home Link
Newsletter 15

Some New Words We've Learned

Clothing
- sandal
- coat
- pants
- dress
- sock
- sweater

Outside Words
- bridge
- farm
- sky
- land
- clouds
- sun
- river

Other Words
- dentist
- city
- pitcher
- jar
- vase
- drawer
- knife
- glasses
- store
- suitcase

Activity Update

We made a "Criss-Cross Mobile." Ask your child to tell you about the parts of the mobile. When you are outside with your child, talk about how the sky and clouds look, where the sun is casting shadows, and different land forms you see, such as: hills, rivers, mountains.

One or More? Fooler Game

Tell your child, "I am going to try to fool you. I will say a body part that means one or more, and you have to touch it. Let's see if I can fool you!" Then quickly say these body parts. Be sure your child touches both legs if you say legs.

- legs
- tooth
- feet
- leg
- fingers
- teeth
- wrist
- foot
- ears
- eyes
- elbow
- arms

Things to Talk About at Home

Teeth Cleaning
Talk with your child about the difference between baby teeth and permanent teeth. Tell your child that a dentist is a doctor who takes care of teeth. Remind your child how important it is to take care of your teeth. Emphasize that your child needs to brush both top and bottom teeth, in the front and in the back.

Brush Humpty's Teeth
Show your child why it is so important to brush your teeth. Here's what to do:

1. Hard boil an egg.

2. Place the egg in a bowl of dark soda pop or juice for a day.

3. Take the egg out. Look at it with your child. Notice the dark discoloration (plaque).

4. Have your child brush the egg with a toothbrush to remove the "plaque."

Language Fun

My Toothbrush Poem
Teach your child this little toothbrush poem. You can say it together at toothbrush time.

> I have a little toothbrush.
> I hold it very tight.
> I brush my teeth each morning
> And then again at night.

Conexión con la escuela y la casa
Boletín 15

Algunas palabras que hemos aprendido

Ropa
- sandal
- pants
- sock
- coat
- dress
- sweater

Palabras exteriores
- bridge
- sky
- clouds
- river
- farm
- land
- sun

Otras palabras
- dentist
- pitcher
- vase
- knife
- store
- city
- jar
- drawer
- glasses
- suitcase

Actividades de última hora

Hicimos un "Móvil de líneas cruzadas." Pida a su hijo que le hable sobre las partes del móvil. Cuando esté afuera con su hijo, hable sobre cómo se ve el cielo y las nubes, dónde está el Sol formando las sombras y diferentes accidentes geográficos que usted ve como colinas, ríos, montañas.

¿Uno o más? Juego de engaño

Diga a su hijo, "Voy a tratar de engañarte. Diré una parte del cuerpo que significa uno o más y tú tienes que tocarla. ¡Déjame ver si te puedo engañar!" Luego, diga esas partes del cuerpo rápidamente. Asegúrese que su hijo toque ambas piernas si usted dice piernas.

- legs
- leg
- wrist
- eyes
- tooth
- fingers
- foot
- elbow
- feet
- teeth
- ears
- arms

Cosas sobre qué conversar en el hogar

Limpieza de los dientes

Hable con su hijo sobre la diferencia entre los dientes de leche y los dientes permanentes. Dígale a su hijo que un dentista es un médico que cuida los dientes. Recuérdele qué tan importante es cuidar sus dientes. Enfatice que su hijo necesita cepillar tanto los dientes de arriba como los de abajo, al frente y atrás.

El cepillo de dientes de Humpty

Muestre a su hijo por qué es tan importante cepillarse los dientes. Esto es lo que hay que hacer:

1. Sancoche un huevo.

2. Coloque el huevo en un tazón con un refresco oscuro o jugo por un día.

3. Saque el huevo. Obsérvelo con su hijo. Note la decoloración oscura (placa).

4. Pídale a su hijo que cepille el huevo con un cepillo de dientes para remover la "placa."

Diviértete con el lenguaje

Mi poema del cepillo de dientes

Enseñe a su hijo este pequeño poema del cepillo de dientes. Pueden decirlo juntos a la hora de cepillarse los dientes.

I have a little toothbrush.
I hold it very tight.
I brush my teeth each morning
And then again at night.

School-Home Link
Newsletter 16

Some New Words We've Learned

More Food
- pie
- cookies
- salad
- ice cream cone

Other Words
- blocks
- baby
- firefighter
- roof
- bush
- nail
- hammer
- gloves
- bathing suit

Activity Update

We made a paper traffic light. See if your child can tell you what the colors mean. Red means STOP. Yellow means MOVE CAREFULLY. Green means GO.

Red Light-Green Light Game

Here's a traffic-light game you can play with your child.

1. Assign your child a starting point across the room from you.

2. Call out one of the traffic light colors (red=stop, green=go, yellow=move carefully).

3. Check to see if your child moves accordingly.

4. If your child makes the wrong move, he or she must go back to the starting point.

Big or Small? Game

Play this word game with your child. Say, "A *roof* is *big*, a *nail* is *small*. A *refrigerator* is *big*, a *penny* is *small*." Your child can think of other examples. Take turns finishing sentences. For example: you say, "A *tree* is *big*…" Your child says, "A *flower* is *small*."

Things to Talk About at Home
Traffic Light Safety

While you and your child are out walking or driving, see if your child can tell you what color the traffic lights are showing. Talk about what each color means. Tell your child that it is safe to cross the street only when the light is red for the traffic to STOP. Remind your child not to cross a street without an adult.

Fire Safety

Tell your child that a firefighter is a person who has the job of putting out fires. Talk about what you and your child would do if a fire occurred at your house. Develop an escape plan and review it often. Teach your child the 911 emergency number.

Language Fun
Traffic Light Song

Here's a little song you can sing together to help your child learn what the traffic light colors mean. Sing it to the tune of "Mary Had a Little Lamb."

> Can you see the traffic light,
> Traffic light, traffic light?
> Green means GO,
> And yellow means SLOW,
> And red means STOP, STOP, STOP!

Spanish Time

Here's a poem about riding in the car.

> **El coche de papá**
> En el coche de papá, nos iremos a pasear.
> Vamos de paseo, pi-pi-pi,
> En un coche, pi-pi-pi,
> Pero no me importa, pi-pi-pi,
> Porque llevo tortas, pi-pi-pi.

Conexión con la escuela y la casa
Boletín 16

Algunas palabras que hemos aprendido

Más alimentos
- pie
- cookies
- salad
- ice cream cone

Otras palabras
- blocks
- baby
- firefighter
- roof
- bush
- nail
- hammer
- gloves
- bathing suit

Actividades de última hora

Hicimos un semáforo de papel. Vea si su hijo le puede decir qué significan los colores. Rojo significa ALTO. Amarillo significa AVANZAR CON CUIDADO. Verde significa AVANZAR.

El juego de la luz roja y verde
A continuación encontrará un juego del semáforo que puede jugar con su hijo.

1. Asígnele a su hijo un punto de partida al otro lado del cuarto de donde usted está.

2. Nombre una de las luces de color del semáforo. (rojo=alto, verde=avanzar, amarillo=avanzar con cuidado)

3. Verifique si su hijo se mueve coordinadamente.

4. Si su hijo se equivoca en el movimiento, él o ella debe regresar al punto de partida.

El juego de ¿grande o pequeño?

Juegue este juego de palabras con su hijo. Diga, "Un *techo* es *grande,* una *uña* es *pequeña.* Un *refrigerador* es *grande*, una *moneda de un centavo* es *pequeña.*" Su hijo puede pensar en otros ejemplos. Túrnense terminando oraciones. Por ejemplo: usted dice, "Un árbol es *grande…*"Su hijo dice, "Una flor es pequeña."

Cosas sobre qué conversar en el hogar
Seguridad en los semáforos
Mientras usted y su hijo se encuentran afuera caminando o manejando, vea si su hijo puede decirle cuáles son los colores que los semáforos están mostrando. Hable sobre qué significa cada color. Diga a su hijo que es seguro cruzar la calle sólo cuando la luz está en rojo para que el tráfico se detenga. Recuérdele de no cruzar la calle sin un adulto.

Seguridad en los incendios
Diga a su hijo que un bombero es una persona que apaga los incendios. Hable sobre qué harían usted y su hijo si llegase a ocurrir un incendio en su casa. Desarrolle un plan de escape y repáselo a menudo. Enseñe a su hijo el número de emergencia 911.

Diviértete con el lenguaje
La canción del semáforo
A continuación encontrará una pequeña canción que puede cantar con su hijo para ayudarlo a entender qué significan los colores del semáforo. Cántela con la melodía de "Mary Had a Little Lamb".

> Can you see the traffic light,
> Traffic light, traffic light?
> Green means GO,
> And yellow means SLOW,
> And red means STOP, STOP, STOP!

La hora del español
A continuación encontrará un poema sobre pasear en el carro.

El coche de papá
> En el coche de papá, nos iremos a pasear.
> Vamos de paseo, pi-pi-pi,
> En un coche, pi-pi-pi,
> Pero no me importa, pi-pi-pi,
> Porque llevo tortas, pi-pi-pi.

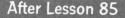

School-Home Link
Newsletter 17

Some New Words We've Learned

- teacher
- Earth
- can
- paper clip
- refrigerator
- coin
- forest
- lion
- ankle
- sheep
- scissors
- spoon
- garbage can
- wrench
- belt
- barn

Activity Update

Your child made a paper refrigerator and filled it with pictures of food. Ask your child to tell you the names of the foods inside the paper refrigerator. Talk about where the foods are in the refrigerator. Is something on the *top, middle,* or *bottom* shelf?

Grocery Chore

When you come home from the grocery store, ask your child to help you put away the groceries. See if your child can identify the different foods. Ask your child if a food item needs to go in the refrigerator or the cupboard. When putting something in the refrigerator or cupboard, talk about where you are putting it. For example: you might say, "I'm putting the sugar on the *middle* shelf." Use the terms *top, middle, bottom, next to, in front of,* and *in back of.*

What's It Made Of?

Your child has been learning materials things are made of. Walk around your house together; ask your child to point out things made of *cloth, plastic, paper, wood, glass,* or *metal.*

Things to Talk About at Home

Who is the Teacher?

Ask your child to tell you his or her teacher's name. Talk to your child about what a teacher does. Encourage your child to "play school" with you, brothers and sisters, or friends. "Playing school" helps your child understand school rules and procedures, and helps your child review what has been learned in the classroom.

I Am Going to the Store and I Will Buy Some...

Here's a game that will help your child learn to remember a sequence of words.

1. Tell your child, "I am going to the store, and I will buy <u>milk</u>."

2. Ask your child to repeat that sentence and add another item. For example: your child might say, "I am going to the store, and I will buy <u>milk</u> and <u>cheese</u>."

3. Continue taking turns adding items until the game gets too difficult.

4. As your child gets better at the game, more items can be added.

What's the Order?

Put four kitchen items or toys on the table. Let your child look at them for about 10 seconds. Ask your child to turn around and not peek while you rearrange the items. Now ask your child to look at the table and "fix it like it was."

Conexión con la escuela y la casa
Boletín 17

Algunas palabras que hemos aprendido

- teacher
- Earth
- can
- paper clip
- refrigerator
- coin
- forest
- lion
- ankle
- sheep
- scissors
- spoon
- garbage can
- wrench
- belt
- barn

Actividades de última hora

Su hijo hizo un refrigerador de papel y lo llenó con ilustraciones de alimentos. Pídale a su hijo que le diga los nombres de los alimentos que están dentro del refrigerador de papel. Hablen sobre el lugar donde están los alimentos en el refrigerador. ¿Es algo que está en la bandeja de *arriba*, del *medio* o de *abajo*?

Tarea de supermercado

Cuando regrese a casa del supermercado, pídale a su hijo que lo ayude a guardar los artículos en su lugar. Vea si su hijo puede identificar los diferentes tipos de alimentos. Pregúntele si necesita guardar alguno de los alimentos en el refrigerador o en la despensa. Cuando coloque algo en el refrigerador o en la despensa, hable acerca de dónde lo coloca. Por ejemplo: usted pudiera decir, "Estoy colocando el azúcar en la bandeja del medio." Use los términos *arriba, medio, abajo, al lado, frente de* y *detrás de*.

¿De qué está hecho?

Su hijo ha aprendido acerca de los materiales de los que están hechos las cosas. Caminen por la casa; pídale a su hijo que señale cosas que estén hechas de *tela, plástico, papel, madera, vidrio* o *metal*.

Cosas sobre qué conversar en el hogar
¿Quién es el maestro?

Pídale a su hijo que le diga el nombre de su maestro. Dígale sobre lo que hace un maestro. Anime a su hijo a "jugar a la escuela" con usted, con sus hermanos o hermanas o con sus amigos. "Jugar a la escuela" ayuda a su hijo a comprender las reglas y los procedimientos escolares, y ayuda a su hijo a repasar lo que ha aprendido en el salón de clases.

Voy a la tienda y compraré un poco de...

Aquí hay un juego que ayudará a su hijo a recordar una secuencia de palabras.

1. Dígale a su hijo: "Voy a la tienda y compraré <u>leche</u>".

2. Pídale a su hijo que repita esa oración y agregue otro artículo. Por ejemplo, su hijo pudiera decir: "Voy a la tienda y compraré <u>leche</u> y <u>queso</u>".

3. Sigan turnándose y agreguen artículos hasta que el juego se haga muy difícil.

4. A medida que su hijo mejora en el juego, se pueden agregar más artículos.

¿Cuál es el orden?

Ponga cuatro artículos de cocina o juguetes en la mesa. Deje que su hijo los observe durante 10 segundos. Pídale a su hijo que se voltee y que no vea mientras usted vuelve a ordenar los artículos. Ahora pídale a su hijo que observe la mesa y "la arregle como estaba".

School-Home Link
Newsletter 18

Some New Words We've Learned

More Animals
- chicken
- zebra
- whale
- seal

Other Words
- ocean
- baseball glove
- boot
- wool
- hair
- saddle
- milk
- package

Activity Update

Your child has been learning about materials things are made of. Ask your child what a boot is made of. Then ask what other things are made of leather.

Blindfold Game

Collect some small objects made of various materials. Some examples might be: a plastic toy, a juice glass, a leather billfold, a metal fork, a sock, a piece of paper. Blindfold your child and put the objects on the table. Ask your child to feel them and guess what material the objects are made of. After the guesses have been made, take off the blindfold and let your child look at the objects.

Take Away

Find some containers such as: a basket, box, bag, jar, bowl. Put them on the table along with a few objects that are not containers, such as: a towel, a piece of jewelry, a toy. Say the rule together, "If you can put something in it, it's a container." Ask your child to take away all the items that are not containers.

Things to Talk About at Home

Down on the Farm

Your child has been learning about farm animals. Ask your child to tell you the names of some animals that live on a farm. Then give your child some animal names and ask whether or not they live on a farm or not. For example: you say, "Does a bear live on a farm?" Your child should answer, "No, a bear doesn't live on a farm."

Where Do We Get Milk?

Ask your child these questions about farm animals:

1. What animal gives us milk? (cow)
2. What animal gives us eggs? (chicken)
3. What animal gives us wool? (sheep)

Language Fun

Whale Bubbles

Talk with your child about whales. They are the biggest animals on Earth, and they live only in the ocean. Your child can have fun making whale bubbles. You will need a dishpan or large bowl and a plastic meat tray. Cut a circle in the center of the plastic tray. Put the following ingredients in the pan:

    2 cups warm water
    ½ cup dishwashing liquid
    2 teaspoons salt

Stir until the salt dissolves. Have your child lay the plastic tray in the bubble solution. Then he or she can pick up the tray and blow on the hole or fan the tray through the air to create whale bubbles!

Conexión con la escuela y la casa
Boletín 18

Algunas palabras que hemos aprendido

Más animales
- chicken
- zebra
- whale
- seal

Otras palabras
- ocean
- baseball glove
- boot
- wool
- hair
- saddle
- milk
- package

Actividades de última hora

Su hijo ha aprendido acerca de los materiales de los que están hechos las cosas. Pregúntele a su hijo de qué está hecha una bota. Luego pregúntele qué otras cosas están hechas de cuero.

El juego de la venda

Reúna algunos objetos pequeños hechos de varios materiales. Algunos ejemplos pudieran ser: un juguete de plástico, un vaso de jugo, una cartera de cuero, un tenedor de metal, un calcetín, un pedazo de papel. Colóquele una venda a su hijo en los ojos y ponga los objetos sobre la mesa. Pídale a su hijo que los toque y que adivine de qué material están hechos. Después de que diga sus suposiciones, quítele la venda y deje que su hijo observe los objetos.

Retirar

Busque algunos recipientes como: una cesta, una caja, una bolsa, una jarra, un tazón. Póngalos sobre la mesa junto con unos cuantos objetos que no sean recipientes, como: una toalla, una joya, un juguete. Digan juntos la regla, "Si puedes poner algo adentro, es un recipiente." Pídale a su hijo que retire todos los artículos que no sean recipientes.

Cosas sobre qué conversar en el hogar

En la granja

Su hijo ha aprendido sobre los animales de una granja. Pídale que le diga los nombres de algunos animales que viven en una granja. Luego, dígale algunos nombres de animales y pregúntele si viven o no en una granja. Por ejemplo, usted dice: "¿Un oso vive en una granja?" Su hijo debe contestar: "No, un oso no vive en una granja".

¿De dónde proviene la leche?

Pregúntele a su hijo estas preguntas sobre los animales de una granja:

1. ¿Qué animal nos da leche? (vaca)

2. ¿Qué animal nos da huevos? (gallina)

3. ¿Qué animal nos da lana? (oveja)

Diviértete con el lenguaje

Bombas de ballena

Hable con su hijo sobre las ballenas. Son los animales más grandes de la Tierra y viven sólo en el océano. Su hijo se puede divertir haciendo bombas de ballena. Usted necesitará una pileta o tazón grande y una bandeja para carne de plástico. Recorte un círculo en el centro de la bandeja de plástico. Ponga los siguientes ingredientes en la pileta:

2 tazas de agua tibia
½ taza de jabón para lavar platos
2 cucharaditas de sal

Revuelva hasta que se disuelva la sal. Pídale a su hijo que coloque la bandeja en la solución jabonosa. Luego él o ella puede levantar la bandeja y soplar a través del hueco o abanicar la bandeja por el aire para crear ¡bombas de ballena!

School-Home Link
Newsletter 19

Some New Words We've Learned
- carpenter
- bugs
- orchard

Activity Update
Your child has been learning the parts of a house. Ask your child to name the parts of a house using the paper house he or she made in school. Parts should include: window, wall, door, roof.

I Am Thinking of...
When you and your child walk in your neighborhood, play a guessing game about parts of houses you see. Give your child clues about a part of a building you are passing. For example: you might say, "I am thinking of something that is brown. It has a knob on it. It opens and shuts." Continue giving clues until your child guesses *door*. Let your child take a turn giving you clues about a part of a building.

Farm or Not Farm?
With your child, look at picture books that have many animal pictures. Point to an animal and ask your child, "Farm or not farm?" If it is a farm animal ask your child, "What do we get from this animal?" Your child should know that milk comes from cows, eggs come from chickens, and wool comes from sheep.

Things to Talk About at Home

A Carpenter
Ask your child to tell you what a carpenter is. (A carpenter is a person who builds things out of wood.) Walk through your home with your child. Ask your child to tell you what items are made of wood.

An Orchard
Ask your child to tell you what an orchard is. (An orchard is a place where fruit grows.) When you are in the grocery store, ask your child to name some of the fruits you see there. When you serve fruit with a meal, ask your child to name the fruit.

Where Do I Live?
Talk with your child about why it is important to know where you live. Teach your child your address. First, teach only the house number. Next, teach the street name. Last, teach the entire address so your child can say, for example: "I live at 25 Maple Street, Los Altos, California."

Language Fun
Here is a little fingerplay you can do with your child.

Homes
This is a nest for Mr. Bluebird.
(Cup both hands together.)
This is a hive for Mrs. Bee.
(Put fists together to form a hive.)
This is a hole for bunny rabbit.
(Hold fingers loosely in a circle.)
And this is a house for me.
(Put fingertips together to form a roof.)

Conexión con la escuela y la casa
Boletín 19

Algunas palabras que hemos aprendido
- carpenter
- bugs
- orchard

Actividades de última hora

Su hijo ha aprendido las partes de una casa. Pida a su hijo que nombre las partes de una casa usando la casa de papel que él o ella hizo en la escuela. Las partes deben incluir: una ventana, una pared, una puerta, un techo.

Estoy pensando en...

Cuando usted y su hijo caminen por el vecindario, jueguen un juego de adivinanzas sobre partes de casas que ve. Dé a su hijo pistas sobre una parte de un edificio por el cual esté pasando. Por ejemplo: usted puede ser que diga, "Estoy pensando en algo que es marrón. Tiene una perilla en él. Se abre y cierra." Continúe dando pistas hasta que su hijo adivine la *puerta*. Deje que su hijo tome un turno y que le dé pistas a usted sobre una parte de un edificio.

¿Es de granja o no?

Con su hijo, observe los libros que tienen muchas ilustraciones de animales. Señale a un animal y pregúntele: "¿es de granja o no?"

Si es un animal de granja pregunte a su hijo: "¿Qué obtenemos de este animal?" Su hijo debe saber que la leche proviene de las vacas, los huevos provienen de las gallinas y la lana proviene de las ovejas.

Cosas sobre qué conversar en el hogar
Un carpintero
Pida que su hijo le diga qué es un carpintero. (Un carpintero es una persona que construye cosas de la madera.) Camine por su casa con su hijo. Pida a su hijo que le diga qué artículos se hacen de la madera.

Un huerto
Pida a su hijo que le diga qué es un huerto. (Un huerto es un lugar donde la crecen las frutas.) Cuando usted esté en la tienda, pídale a su hijo que nombre algunas de las frutas que usted ve allí. Cuando usted sirva la fruta con una comida, pida a su hijo que nombre la fruta.

¿Dónde vivo?

Hable con su hijo sobre por qué es importante saber dónde vive usted. Enseñe a su hijo su dirección. Primero, enséñele solamente el número de casa. Después, enséñele el nombre de la calle. Por último, enséñele la dirección completa de manera que su hijo pueda decir, por ejemplo: "Yo vivo en el número 25 de la calle Maple, Los Altos, California."

Diviértete con el lenguaje

A continuación encontrará un pequeño juego de dedos que puede jugar con su hijo.

Homes
This is a nest for Mr. Bluebird.
(Coloca las manos en forma de una taza.)
This is a hive for Mrs. Bee.
(Une los puños para formar una colmena.)
This is a hole for bunny rabbit.
(Forma un círculo con los dedos y que a penas se toquen.)
And this is a house for me.
(Junta los dedos para formar un techo.)

School-Home Link
Newsletter 20

Activity Update

Your child has been learning about a carpenter and the tools a carpenter uses. Ask your child to show you the paper carpenter he or she made, and then tell you the names of the tools (ladder, nail, wrench, hammer, and ruler).

Name That Tool!

If you have hand tools in your home, lay some of them out on the table. Ask your child to name as many of them as possible. Talk about how each tool is used. Tell your child that tools need to be used safely. Saws have sharp edges that can cut fingers. Hammers can pound nails, but they can pound fingers, too! Remind your child not to touch tools unless an adult is there to supervise.

Some, All, or None

Your child has been learning about *some, all,* and *none.* Put an assortment of small toys or kitchen objects on a table. Use a towel or scarf to cover up *some, all,* or *none* of the objects. Ask your child to tell you what you have covered using a complete sentence. For example: your child might say, "You covered up *all* of the toys."

Language Fun

Read the story "The Three Little Pigs" to your child. Talk about the kinds of materials the pigs used to build their houses. Let your child identify the building materials shown in the pictures.

Things to Talk About at Home

Address and Phone Number

Have your child repeat your address to you. Then ask for your telephone number. Review these important pieces of information often.

Look and Remember

Play this memory game with your child to help review the materials that objects are made of. Tell your child to look around the room to find as many objects as possible that are made of *cloth*. Ask your child to name the cloth objects. Then, tell your child, "Close your eyes and tell me how many things you can remember that are made of cloth. No peeking!" Try the game with these other materials: wood, plastic, metal, glass, leather.

Build a Room

Help your child learn to classify and sort pictures. Here's what to do:

1. Discuss with your child what items you will find in a kitchen, bedroom, or family room.

2. Use catalogs or magazines to find pictures of items that belong in the room you have chosen.

3. Have your child cut out the pictures and glue them on a piece of paper or in a shoebox.

4. Ask your child to tell you the names of the items in the pictures.

Conexión con la escuela y la casa
Boletín 20

Actividades de última hora

Su hijo ha aprendido sobre un carpintero y las herramientas que usa un carpintero. Pídale a su hijo que le muestre el carpintero de papel que hizo y luego que le diga el nombre de las herramientas (escalera, clavo, llave inglesa, martillo y regla).

¡Nombra esa herramienta!

Si usted tiene herramientas manuales en su casa, coloque algunas sobre la mesa. Pídale a su hijo que nombre tantas como sea posible. Hable de cómo se usa cada una. Dígale a su hijo que las herramientas se deben usar con cuidado. Las sierras tienen bordes afilados que pueden cortar dedos. Los martillos pueden machacar clavos, pero también pueden machacar dedos. Recuérdele a su hijo que no debe tocar herramientas a menos de que un adulto esté allí para supervisar.

Algunos, todos o ninguno

Su hijo ha aprendido acerca de *algunos, todos* y *ninguno*. Ponga un surtido de juguetes pequeños u objetos de cocina sobre una mesa. Use una toalla o bufanda para cubrir *algunos, todos* o *ninguno* de los objetos. Pídale a su hijo que le diga lo que ha tapado usando una oración completa. Por ejemplo, su hijo pudiera decir: "Tú tapaste todos los juguetes."

Diviértete con el lenguaje

Léale el cuento de The "Three Little Pigs" a su hijo. Hable sobre los tipos de materiales que usaron los cerditos para construir sus casas. Deje que su hijo identifique los materiales de construcción que se muestran en las ilustraciones.

Cosas sobre qué conversar en el hogar
Dirección y número telefónico

Pídale a su hijo que le repita su dirección. Luego, pregúntele su número telefónico. A menudo, repase esta información importante.

Observa y recuerda

Juegue con su hijo este juego de memoria para ayudarlo a repasar los materiales de los que están hechos los objetos. Dígale a su hijo que observe la habitación y que halle tantos objetos como sea posible que estén hechos de tela. Pídale que nombre los objetos de *tela*. Luego, dígale a su hijo: "Cierra los ojos y dime cuántas cosas puedes recordar que son hechas de tela. ¡No hagas trampa!" Intente el juego con estos otros materiales: madera, plástico, metal, vidrio, cuero.

Construir un salón

Ayude a su hijo a aprender a clasificar y ordenar ilustraciones. Aquí está lo que tiene que hacer:

1. Comente con su hijo los objetos que hallará en una cocina, una habitación o un salón familiar.

2. Use catálogos o revistas para hallar ilustraciones de artículos que pertenecen en el salón que ha elegido.

3. Pídale a su hijo que recorte las ilustraciones y las pegue en una hoja o en una caja de zapatos.

4. Pídale a su hijo que le diga los nombres de los artículos de las ilustraciones.

School-Home Link
Newsletter 21

Some New Words We've Learned

Buildings
- church
- gas station
- school
- theater
- apartment building
- skyscraper

Activity Update

Your child has been learning about containers. We made a mailbox and an envelope to go in it. Ask your child to explain to you what happens to an envelope when you put it in a mailbox.

Mail a Picture

Help your child send a picture to a friend or relative. Ask your child to draw a picture. Let your child put the picture in an envelope. Talk about what you must do before putting the envelope in a mailbox. Show your child how you write the address and put on the stamp. Talk about how the envelope will get to the friend or relative.

Building Hunt

When you and your child are out driving or walking through your community, look at the many kinds of buildings you see. Ask your child to tell you the names of different buildings. Ask your child to tell you what each building is used for.

Things to Talk About at Home

My Birthday Is...
Your child has been learning the names of the months. Help your child practice saying his or her birthdate. Ask your child to say this sentence and complete it: "My birthday is _____."

Coats and Shoes
Your child has been learning the parts of a coat and a shoe. Help your child practice the names of the parts. When your child puts on a coat, ask him or her to name the parts (front, back, buttons, collar, pockets, sleeves). Then ask, "What is the whole object called?" (Coat.)

When your child puts on a shoe, ask him or her to name the parts (heel, sole, tongue, lace, top). Then ask, "What is the whole object called?" (Shoe.)

Tell Me Another!

Your child has learned classes, such as: vehicles, food, containers, clothing, animals, buildings. Choose a class and give your child several examples in that class. Then ask your child to "Tell me another...." For example: say, "Truck, car, taxi, tell me another." (Bus, train, plane, and so on.) Or choose food and say, "Cheese, apple, chicken, tell me another." (Bread, banana, ice cream, and so on.)

Conexión con la escuela y la casa

Boletín 21

Algunas palabras que hemos aprendido

Edificaciones

- church
- gas station
- school
- theater
- apartment building
- skyscraper

Actividades de última hora

Su hijo ha aprendido sobre recipientes. Hicimos un buzón de correos y un sobre para colocarlo adentro de éste. Pídale a su hijo que le explique qué le sucede a un sobre cuando lo pone en un buzón de correos.

Enviar un dibujo

Ayude a su hijo a enviar un dibujo a un amigo o familiar. Pídale que haga un dibujo. Deje que su hijo ponga el dibujo dentro de un sobre. Hable acerca de lo que debe hacer antes de colocar el sobre en un buzón. Muéstrele a su hijo cómo escribe la dirección y pone la estampilla. Hable sobre cómo el sobre llegará al amigo o familiar.

Cacería de edificios

Cuando usted y su hijo salen en el carro o caminan por su comunidad, observen los diferentes tipos de edificios que ven. Pídale a su hijo que le diga los nombres de los diferentes tipos de edificios. Pídale a su hijo que le diga para qué se usa cada tipo de edificio.

Cosas sobre qué conversar en el hogar

Mi cumpleaños es...

Su hijo ha aprendido los nombres de los meses. Ayude a su hijo a practicar diciendo su fecha de cumpleaños. Pídale a su hijo que diga esta oración y la complete: "Mi cumpleaños es _____."

Abrigos y zapatos

Su hijo ha aprendido las partes de un abrigo y un zapato. Ayude a su hijo a practicar los nombres de las partes. Cuando su hijo se ponga un abrigo, pídale que nombre las partes (parte de enfrente, parte de atrás, botones, cuello, bolsillos, mangas). Luego pregunte: "¿Cómo se llama el objeto?" (Abrigo.)

Cuando su hijo se ponga un zapato, pídale que nombre las partes (tacón, suela, lengüeta, lazo, parte de arriba). Luego pregunte: "¿Cómo se llama el objeto?" (Zapato.)

¡Dime otro!

Su hijo ha aprendido sobre clases, como: vehículos, comida, recipientes, ropa, animales, edificios. Elija una clase y dé a su hijo varios ejemplos de esa clase. Luego pídale a su hijo que le "diga otro...." Por ejemplo: diga, "Camión, carro, taxi, dime otro." (Autobús, tren, avión y así sucesivamente.) O elija una comida y diga, "Queso, manzana, pollo, dime otro." (Pan, banana, helado y así sucesivamente.)

School-Home Link
Newsletter 22

Some New Words We've Learned

Visiting the Doctor's Office
- doctor
- nurse
- patient

Other Words
- pin
- tire
- hose

Activity Update

We played a game called "Going Places" to help us think about how vehicles can be used to go different places. Help your child practice by asking questions like, "What vehicle takes you to school?" (bus); "What vehicle could take you across water?" (boat); "What vehicle does your grandmother drive?" (car); "What vehicle pulls lots of cars full of different things?" (train)

Parts of a Chair, Parts of a Tree

If you have a wood chair, ask your child to identify the parts (legs, back, seat, rungs). When you are outside near a tree, ask your child to identify the parts of the tree (branches, leaves, trunk, roots). Choose something else that has parts. Help your child learn the names of the parts.

Spanish Time

Here's a fun little poem you and your child can say together.

> Un ratoncito
> iba por un arado
> y este cuentecito
> ya se ha acabado.

Things to Talk About at Home

Doctor
Ask your child, "What do we call a person who helps people get well?" (A doctor.) Then ask your child to, "Say the whole thing about a doctor." (A doctor is a person who helps people get well.) Discuss with your child why it is important to visit a doctor when you are sick, as well as to get regular check-ups.

Months of the Year

Your child has been learning to say the months of the year, starting with January. Say the names of the months with your child. Talk about what month it is now and what special things you might do this month. Then talk about what next month will be and what will be happening then.

Language Fun

Here is a fun song to sing to help your child learn how important it is to wash your hands. Sing it to the tune of "Row, Row, Row Your Boat."

Wash, Wash, Wash Your Hands
Wash, wash, wash your hands,
Play our hand game.
Rub and scrub, and scrub and rub,
Germs go down the drain. Hey!
Wash, wash, wash your hands,
Play our hand game.
Rub and scrub, and scrub and rub,
Dirt goes down the drain. Hey!

Conexión con la escuela y la casa
Boletín 22

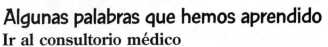

Algunas palabras que hemos aprendido
Ir al consultorio médico
- doctor
- nurse
- patient

Otras palabras
- pin
- hose
- tire

Actividades de última hora
Jugamos un juego llamado "Ir a pasear" para ayudarnos a pensar cómo se pueden usar los vehículos para ir a diversos lugares. Ayude a practicar a su hijo haciendo preguntas como, "¿Qué vehículo te lleva a la escuela?" (autobús); "¿Qué vehículo podría llevarte por el agua?" (barco); "¿Qué vehículo maneja tu abuela?" (coche); "¿Qué vehículo jala muchos carros lleno de diversas cosas?" (tren)

Partes de una silla, partes de un árbol
Si usted tiene una silla de madera, pida a su niño que identifique las partes de la silla (patas, espaldar, asiento, peldaños). Cuando esté afuera, cerca de un árbol, pida a su hijo que identifique las partes del árbol (ramas, hojas, tronco, raíces). Elija algo más que se divida en partes. Ayude a su hijo a aprender los nombres de las partes.

La hora del español
A continuación encontrará un pequeño y gracioso poema que Ud. y su hijo pueden decir juntos.

Un ratoncito
iba por un arado
y este cuentecito
ya se ha acabado.

Cosas sobre qué conversar en el hogar
El médico
Pregunte a su hijo, "¿Cómo llamamos a una persona que ayuda a las personas a que se mejoren?" (un médico) Luego, pida a su hijo que "diga todo sobre un médico." (Un médico es alguien que ayuda a las personas a que se mejoren.) Comente con su hijo por qué es importante visitar a un médico cuando se está enfermo, así como para obtener chequeos regulares.

Meses del año
Su hijo ha aprendido a decir los meses del año, empezando en enero. Diga los meses del año con su hijo. Diga en qué mes estamos ahora y cuáles son las cosas especiales que debe hacer en este mes. Luego hable sobre cuál es el mes que viene y qué pasará luego.

Diviértete con el lenguaje
A continuación encontrará una graciosa canción para que la cante con su hijo y lo ayude a comprender por qué es importante lavarse las manos. Cántela con la melodía de "Row, Row, Row Your Boat."

Wash, Wash, Wash Your Hands
Wash, wash, wash your hands,
Play our hand game.
Rub and scrub, and scrub and rub,
Germs go down the drain. Hey!
Wash, wash, wash your hands,
Play our hand game.
Rub and scrub, and scrub and rub,
Dirt goes down the drain. Hey!

School-Home Link
Newsletter 23

Some New Words We've Learned
- medicine
- cabbage
- police officer
- grass
- saw

Activity Update
We played a game called "First, Next, Last" to help your child learn to follow a sequence of actions. Help your child practice this skill at home. Talk about what you do *first, next,* and *last* in one of your daily activities. For example: ask your child to tell you what he or she does *first, next,* and *last* when getting ready for bed. (First, I put on my pajamas. Next, I brush my teeth. Last, I get into bed.)

Following Directions
Ask your child to perform some chores at home. Use the words *first, next,* and *last.* For example: you might say, "*First,* pick up the ball. *Next,* put your shoes away. *Last,* bring me a book to read to you." If your child forgets a step, repeat the directions.

Follow the Leader
Play "Follow the Leader" to help your child practice *first, next,* and *last.* Here's how to play:

1. The leader says a sequence of three actions. For example: "First, I'll touch my head; next, I'll touch my knee; last, I'll clap my hands. The leader then demonstrates the actions.

2. The follower must follow the same sequence. If he or she does, then the follower gets to take a turn at being the leader.

Things to Talk About at Home
Police Officer
Your child has been learning about a police officer. Ask your child to tell you what a police officer does. (A police officer is a person who helps keep people safe.) Discuss a police officer's duties.

Review with your child what to do in an emergency. Ask your child to repeat your phone number and address. Be sure your child knows how to dial the 911 emergency number.

Before and After
Read a story to your child. Talk about what happens before and after events in the story. For example: if you read "Goldilocks and The Three Bears," talk about what Goldilocks did *before* she tasted the Baby Bear's porridge. Talk about what she did *after* she tried the Mother Bear's chair.

Language Fun
Here's a little poem you and your child can share to remind you about what a police officer does.

Our Friend
The police officer has many jobs.
They never seem to end.
But this you must remember:
The police officer is our friend.

Conexión con la escuela y la casa
Boletín 23

Algunas palabras que hemos aprendido
- medicine
- grass
- cabbage
- saw
- police officer

Actividades de última hora

Jugamos un juego llamado "primero, después, último" para ayudar a su hijo a aprender a seguir una secuencia de acciones. Ayude a su hijo a practicar esta destreza en casa. Hable sobre lo que hace *primero, después* y de *último* en una de sus actividades diarias. Por ejemplo: pida que su hijo le diga qué es lo que él o ella hace *primero, después* y de *último* antes de ir a la cama. (Primero, me pongo mis pijamas. Después, me cepillo los dientes. Y por último, me voy a la cama.)

Seguir instrucciones

Pida a su hijo que realice algunas tareas en la casa. Utilice las palabras *primero, después* y *último*. Por ejemplo, usted podría decir: "*Primero*, recoge la pelota. *Después*, guarda tus zapatos. Y por *último*, tráeme un libro para leértelo." Si su hijo olvida un paso, repita las instrucciones.

Sigue al líder

Juegue "Sigue al líder" para ayudar a su hijo a que practique las palabras *primero, después* y *último*.

Así es cómo se juega:

1. La persona líder dice una secuencia de tres acciones. Por ejemplo: "Primero, tocaré mi cabeza; después, tocaré mis rodillas; por último, aplaudiré. Luego la persona líder, debe demostrar las acciones.

2. Los jugadores deben seguir la misma secuencia. Si él o ella lo hace, el jugador toma el turno y se convierte en la persona líder.

Cosas sobre qué conversar en el hogar
Oficial de policía

Su hijo ha aprendido sobre un oficial de policía. Pida a su hijo que le diga qué es lo que hace un oficial de policía. (Un oficial de policía es alguien que ayuda a que las personas estén fuera de peligro.) Comente los deberes de un oficial de policía.

Repase con su hijo qué hacer en una emergencia. Pida a su hijo que repita su número telefónico y su dirección. Asegúrese de que su hijo sabe cómo marcar el número de emergencia 911.

Antes y después

Léale una historia a su hijo. Hable sobre qué sucede *antes* y *después* en los sucesos de la historia. Por ejemplo: Si usted lee "Goldilocks and The Three Bears," hable sobre qué hizo Goldilocks antes de probar la avena del Bebé Oso. Hable de lo que ella hizo *después* que se sentó en la silla de Mamá Osa.

Diviértete con el lenguaje

A continuación encontrará un pequeño poema que usted y su hijo pueden compartir para recordarle lo que hace un oficial de policía.

Our Friend
The police officer has many jobs.
They never seem to end.
But this you must remember:
The police officer is our friend.

School-Home Link
Newsletter 24

Some New Words We've Learned
- jungle
- passenger
- driver
- beach

Activity Update
We played a game called "Cover Up!" to help your child learn opposites. Help your child learn opposites at home by playing an opposites game. You give your child a word, and your child tells you the opposite. Here are some words you can use:

- full/empty
- wet/dry
- tall/short
- big/small
- long/short
- old/young

What Class Are They In?
Here is a word game you can play with your child. You say, "I am going to name some things that are in the same class. You're going to tell me the class." Name two things in any of these classes: *clothing, vehicles, food, animals, buildings.* For example: you say, "A coat and a sock." Your child says, "Clothing." You say, "Meat and cheese." Your child says, "Food."

Same/Different
Your child has been learning about *same* and *different.* Ask your child to tell you how two things are the same and how they are different. Here are some words to use:

- a fish and a boat
- a bird and an airplane
- a horse and a car

Things to Talk About at Home
The *W* Questions
Read a story to your child. As you read, stop at different times and ask the "*W* Questions" (*Who, When, Where,* and *What*). Give your child some help with the answers if needed. For example: if you read "The Little Red Hen" to your child, you might ask, "Where does this story take place?; Who planted some corn?; What did the hen want the other animals to do?; When did the hen and her chicks eat the corn?"

Jungle
Your child has been learning about the jungle. Ask your child to tell you what a jungle is. (A jungle is a forest in a hot place.) Talk about what animals might live in a jungle (tiger, monkey, parrot, snake, lizard). You can play a game by giving your child some animal names. Let your child tell you whether or not the animal would live in the jungle.

Language Fun
Read your child a book about jungle animals. See how many animals your child can identify. Here are two titles:

Walking Through the Jungle by Julie Lacome
Jungle Animals by Angela Royston

Ask your librarian for more books about the jungle.

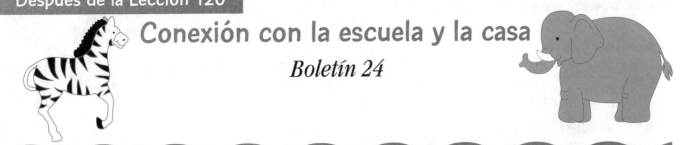

Conexión con la escuela y la casa
Boletín 24

Algunas palabras que hemos aprendido
- jungle
- passenger
- driver
- beach

Actividades de última hora

Jugamos un juego llamado "¡Taparlo!" para ayudar a su hijo a aprender sobre opuestos. Ayude a su hijo a aprender sobre opuestos en la casa, jugando un juego de opuestos. Usted le da a su hijo una palabra y su hijo le dice el opuesto. Aquí hay algunas palabras que puede usar:

- full/empty
- wet/dry
- tall/short
- big/small
- long/short
- old/young

¿A qué clase pertenecen?

Aquí hay un juego de palabras que usted puede jugar con su hijo. Usted dice: "Voy a nombrar algunas cosas que están en la misma clase. Tú me vas a decir la clase." Nombra dos cosas en cualquiera de estas clases: *ropa, vehículos, comida, animales, edificios.* Por ejemplo, usted dice: "Un abrigo y un calcetín." Su hijo dice: "Ropa." Usted dice: "Carne y queso." Su hijo dice: "Comida."

Igual/Diferente

Su hijo ha aprendido sobre *igual* y *diferente*. Pídale a su hijo que le diga en qué se parecen dos cosas y en qué se diferencian. Aquí hay algunas palabras que puede usar:

- un pez y un bote
- un ave y un avión
- un caballo y un carro

Cosas sobre qué conversar en el hogar
Las 4 preguntas

Léale un cuento a su hijo. Mientras lee, deténgase varias veces y haga las "4 preguntas"(*Quién, Cuándo, Dónde* y *Qué*). Ayude a su hijo con las respuestas si es necesario. Por ejemplo: si le lee "La gallinita roja" a su hijo, usted podría preguntar: "¿Dónde sucede este cuento?; ¿Quién sembró un poco de maíz?; ¿Qué quería la gallina que los otros animales hicieran?; ¿Cuándo se comieron el maíz la gallina y sus pollitos?"

La selva

Su hijo ha aprendido sobre la selva. Pídale a su hijo que le diga qué es una selva. (Una selva es un bosque en un lugar cálido.) Hable de los animales que pudieran vivir en una selva (tigre, mono, loro, serpiente, lagartija). Usted puede jugar un juego dándole a su hijo algunos nombres de animales. Deje que su hijo le diga si el animal viviría o no en la selva.

Diviértete con el lenguaje

Léale a su hijo un libro sobre animales de la selva. Observe cuántos animales puede identificar su hijo. Aquí hay dos títulos:

Walking Through the Jungle by Julie Lacome
Jungle Animals by Angela Royston

Pídale a su bibliotecario más libros sobre la selva.

School-Home Link
Newsletter 25

Some New Words We've Learned

Tools
- drill
- paintbrush
- pliers
- screwdriver

Other Words
- thermometer
- calendar
- notebook
- lightbulb
- envelope
- painter
- tissue
- magazine
- grocery store
- mirror
- card

Activity Update

Your child made a "Happy/Sad Puppet." Ask your child to show you the happy face. Then ask your child to show you the sad face. Now make it harder. Ask your child to show you the opposite of happy. (Your child should show you the sad face.) Now ask to see the opposite of sad. (Your child should show you the happy face.)

What Is That Tool For?

Show your child some hand tools you have at your house, such as: a hammer, screwdriver, pliers, saw, paintbrush, drill. Talk about how each tool can be used. Give your child examples of jobs and ask which tool to use. For example: to put a picture on the wall (hammer and nail), to cut a board in two (saw), to make a hole for a door in a bird house (drill), to change the color of a wall (paintbrush), to tighten a loose screw (screwdriver), to get a tight lid off of a jar (pliers). Remind your child not to touch tools unless an adult is present.

Things to Talk About at Home

Materials

Your child has been learning about things made with paper. Walk around your house and ask your child to point out and name objects made of paper.

Put a variety of small objects made of different materials on a table. Try to include things made of glass, paper, plastic, leather, wood, metal, and cloth. Ask your child to identify each object, and then tell you what material the object is made of.

Play "Build a Story"

Help your child learn to tell a story. You will need to cut out of a magazine three pictures of people, three pictures of places, and three pictures of activities. Here's how to play:

1. Have your child explain what each picture shows.

2. Tell your child to "build a story" by picking one picture from each group (people, places, activities).

3. Your child can tell a story by telling about the person, what is happening, and where it is happening.

4. Your child can put the pictures back and select three more pictures to tell another story.

Spanish Time

Here's a poem about musical chickens that you and your child can say together.

> Cinco pollitos tiene mi tía.
> Uno le canta, otro le pía.
> Y tres le tocan la sinfonía.

Conexión con la escuela y la casa
Boletín 25

Algunas palabras que hemos aprendido

Herramientas
- drill
- paintbrush
- pliers
- screwdriver

Otras palabras
- thermometer
- calendar
- notebook
- lightbulb
- envelope
- painter
- tissue
- magazine
- grocery store
- mirror
- card

Actividades de última hora

Su hijo hizo un "Títere con una cara feliz y una triste." Pídale a su hijo que le muestre la cara feliz. Luego pídale que le muestre la cara triste. Ahora inténtelo un poco más difícil. Pídale a su hijo que le muestre lo opuesto de feliz. (Su hijo le debe mostrar la cara triste.) Ahora dígale que quiere ver lo opuesto de triste. (Su hijo le debe mostrar la cara feliz.)

¿Para qué es esa herramienta?

Muéstrele a su hijo algunas herramientas manuales que tiene en su casa, como: un martillo, destornillador, alicates, sierra, brocha para pintar, taladro. Hable de cómo se puede usar cada herramienta. Dé ejemplos de trabajos a su hijo y pregunte qué herramienta se debe usar. Por ejemplo: poner un cuadro en la pared (martillo y clavo), cortar una tabla en dos (sierra), hacer un agujero para una puerta en una casa para pájaros (taladro), cambiar el color de una pared (brocha para pintar), apretar un tornillo que está suelto (destornillador), quitarle la tapa a una jarra que está pegada (alicates). Recuérdele a su hijo que no debe tocar las herramientas a menos de que esté presente un adulto.

Cosas sobre qué conversar en el hogar
Materiales

Su hijo ha aprendido sobre cosas hechas de papel. Caminen por la casa y pídale a su hijo que señale y nombre objetos hechos de papel.

Ponga una variedad de objetos pequeños sobre una mesa. Trate de incluir cosas hechas de vidrio, papel, plástico, cuero, madera, metal y tela. Pídale a su hijo que identifique cada objeto y que luego le diga de qué material está hecho el objeto.

Juego de "Inventar un cuento"

Ayude a su hijo a aprender a decir un cuento. Usted necesitará recortar tres fotografías de personas, tres fotografías de lugares y tres fotografías de actividades. Así es como se debe jugar:

1. Pídale a su hijo que explique lo que muestra cada fotografía.

2. Dígale a su hijo que "invente un cuento" al elegir una fotografía de cada grupo (personas, lugares, actividades).

3. Su hijo puede decir un cuento, hablando de la persona, de lo que sucede y dónde sucede.

4. Su hijo puede poner las fotografías donde estaban y elegir tres fotografías más para contar otro cuento.

La hora del español

Aquí hay un poema sobre pollitos musicales que usted y su hijo pueden decir.

Cinco pollitos tiene mi tía.
Uno le canta, otro le pía.
Y tres le tocan la sinfonía.

School-Home Link
Newsletter 26

Some New Words We've Learned

Seasons
- winter
- summer
- spring
- fall

Grocery Store
- shelves
- grocery cart
- checker
- customer
- cash register

Other Words
- stairs
- tractor

Activity Update

We played the "Animal Babies on the Farm" game to help us learn the names of baby farm animals. You can play the game at home with your child. Turn all of the baby animal pictures facedown. Then have your child pick up one card at a time. Your child should name the baby animal and put it on top of its parent in the farm picture. If your child has trouble with the baby animal names, give some help. (sheep–lamb, pig–piglet, cat–kitten, dog–puppy, chicken–chick, horse–foal, goose–gosling, cow–calf)

Books About Seasons

Read a book about the seasons to your child. Look for clues in the pictures as to what season it is. Here are two titles:

The Year at Maple Hill Farm by Alice and Martin Provenson
The Ox-Cart Man by Donald Hall

Ask your librarian for more books about the seasons.

Things to Talk About at Home

Seasons
Your child is learning to name the seasons. Say the seasons with your child, starting with *winter*. Talk about what season it is now. What season comes next? Discuss what the weather is like where you live during the different seasons.

Grocery Store
Your child has been learning about the grocery store. When you and your child go to the grocery store, ask your child to name the different people and objects there (shelves, grocery cart, cash register, customer, checker).

Talk about how the grocery store is organized so that customers can find what they need. Ask your child to identify some of the foods on the shelves.

Language Fun
Have fun singing "Old MacDonald Had a Farm" with your child to practice some of the farm animal names and sounds.

Old MacDonald had a farm, E-I-E-I-O.
And on his farm he had a cow, E-I-E-I-O.
With a moo-moo here,
And a moo-moo there,
Here a moo, there a moo,
Everywhere a moo-moo.
Old MacDonald had a farm, E-I-E-I-O.
(horse–neigh, pig–oink, sheep–bah, chicken–cluck, duck–quack, dog–arf, cat–meow)

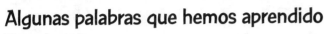

Conexión con la escuela y la casa
Boletín 26

Algunas palabras que hemos aprendido

Estaciones
- winter
- summer
- spring
- fall

Supermercado
- shelves
- grocery cart
- checker
- customer
- cash register

Otras palabras
- stairs
- tractor

Actividades de última hora

Jugamos el juego de "Animales bebés en la granja" para aprender los nombres de los animales bebés de una granja. Usted puede jugarlo en la casa con su hijo. Voltee todas las ilustraciones de los animales bebés boca abajo. Luego, pídale a su hijo que tome una carta a la vez. Su hijo debe nombrar el animal bebé y ponerlo sobre su padre en la ilustración de la granja. Si su hijo tiene problemas con los nombres de los animales bebés, ayúdelo. (oveja–cordero, cerdo–cerdito, gato–gatito, perro–perrito, pollo–pollito, caballo–potro, ganso–ansarino, vaca–becerro)

Libros sobre las estaciones

Léale un libro sobre las estaciones a su hijo. Busque claves en las ilustraciones para decir qué estación es. Aquí hay dos títulos:

The Year at Maple Hill Farm by Alice and Martin Provenson
The Ox-Cart Man by Donald Hall

Pídale a su bibliotecario más libros sobre las estaciones.

Cosas sobre qué conversar en el hogar

Estaciones
Su hijo aprende a nombrar las estaciones. Diga las estaciones con su hijo, comenzando con *invierno*. Hable sobre la estación actual. ¿Qué estación sigue? Comente cómo es el clima donde usted vive durante las diferentes estaciones.

Supermercado
Su hijo ha aprendido sobre el supermercado. Cuando usted y su hijo van al supermercado, pídale a su hijo que nombre a las diferentes personas y los diferentes objetos de allí (estantes, carrito de supermercado, caja registradora, cliente, verificador).

Hable de cómo está organizado el supermercado para que los clientes puedan hallar lo que necesitan. Pídale a su hijo que identifique algunos de los alimentos en los estantes.

Diviértete con el lenguaje
Diviértase cantando "Old MacDonald Had a Farm" con su hijo para practicar algunos de los nombres y sonidos de los animales de la granja.

Old MacDonald had a farm, E-I-E-I-O.
And on his farm he had a cow, E-I-E-I-O.
With a moo-moo here,
And a moo-moo there,
Here a moo, there a moo,
Everywhere a moo-moo.
Old MacDonald had a farm, E-I-E-I-O.
(horse–neigh, pig–oink, sheep–bah, chicken–cluck, duck–quack, dog–arf, cat–meow)

School-Home Link
Newsletter 27

Some New Words We've Learned

Dental Care
- dentist's office
- dentist's chair
- drill
- dental tools

Health Care
- doctor's office
- medicine
- scale
- examining table

Locations
- airport
- fire station

Occupations
- pilot
- lumberjack

Other Words
- bench
- doghouse

Activity Update

We played "Shop Till You Drop!" to learn about buying foods in the grocery store. Ask your child to identify these items in the grocery store picture: checker, customer, shelves, cash register, grocery cart.

Make a Shopping List!

Before you take your child to the grocery store, discuss the food that you need to buy. Look through the newspaper ads and cut out pictures of foods you need, or circle them with a pen. When you get to the store, see if your child can remember where certain foods can be found. For example: you might ask, "Where will we find the ice cream?"

Spanish Time

Sing "The Itsy Bitsy Spider" in Spanish with your child.

> La araña pequeñita subió, subió, subió,
> Vino la lluvia y se la llevó.
> Salió el sol y todo lo secó,
> Y la araña pequeñita subió, subió, subió.

Things to Talk About at Home

Bigger and Smaller
Your child has been learning about *bigger* and *smaller.* You can help your child practice these words. Put a variety of different sized objects on a table. You might use a book, pencil, spoon, penny, plate, a big toy, a small toy, and so on. Ask your child to choose two objects and then tell you which is bigger or smaller. For example: your child might choose the penny and the cup and say, "The penny is smaller than the cup," or "The cup is bigger than the penny." Continue until you have used all of the objects.

Follow the Leader

Go on a furniture hunt with your child. Walk through your home and say, "Let's touch and name furniture. I have to remember the names and the order of the furniture you touch." Have your child touch four or more pieces of furniture. As each piece is touched, you say the name. Then repeat the names in order. Next, have your child be the leader and remember the names and order of all the furniture you touch.

Language Fun

Read a book to your child about something big and something small. Ask your child to point out what is bigger and what is smaller. Here are some titles:

The Lion and the Mouse Aesop's Fable
Little Penguin by Patrick Benson
Where's My Teddy? by Jez Alborough

Conexión con la escuela y la casa
Boletín 27

Algunas palabras que hemos aprendido

Cuidado dental
- dentist's office
- drill
- dentist's chair
- dental tools

Cuidado de la salud
- doctor's office
- scale
- medicine
- examining table

Ubicaciones
- airport
- fire station

Ocupaciones
- pilot
- lumberjack

Otras palabras
- bench
- doghouse

Actividades de última hora

Jugamos "¡Comprar hasta más no poder!" para aprender sobre comprar alimentos en el supermercado. Pida a su hijo que identifique estos artículos en la ilustración del supermercado: cajero, cliente, estantes, caja registradora, carro de comestibles.

¡Hacer una lista de compras!

Antes de que usted lleve a su hijo a la tienda de comestibles, comente el alimento que necesita comprar. Mire los anuncios del periódico y recorte las ilustraciones de los alimentos que necesita o enciérrelos en un círculo con un bolígrafo. Cuando esté en la tienda, vea si su hijo puede recordar dónde se pueden hallar ciertos alimentos. Por ejemplo: usted podría preguntar, "¿Dónde encontraremos el helado?"

La hora del español

Cante en español con su hijo "La araña pequeñita"

La araña pequeñita subió, subió, subió,
Vino la lluvia y se la llevó.
Salió el sol y todo lo secó,
Y la araña pequeñita subió, subió, subió.

Cosas sobre qué conversar en el hogar

Más grande y más pequeño

Su hijo ha aprendido sobre lo que significa *más grande* y *más pequeño*. Usted puede ayudar a su hijo a practicar estas palabras. Coloque sobre la mesa una variedad de objetos de diferentes tamaños. Puede usar un libro, un lápiz, una cuchara, un *penny,* un plato, un juguete grande, un juguete pequeño y así sucesivamente. Pida a su hijo que elija dos objetos y que luego le diga cuál es el más grande y cuál es el más pequeño. Por ejemplo: quizás su hijo elija el *penny* y la taza y luego diga, "El *penny* es más pequeño que la taza" o "La taza es más grande que el *penny.*" Continúe hasta que haya usado todos los objetos.

Sigue al líder

Vaya en una cacería de muebles con su hijo. Camine por su casa y diga: "Toquemos y nombremos muebles. Tengo que recordar los nombres y el orden de los muebles que tocas." Pida a su hijo que toque cuatro o más muebles. A medida que toque cada uno, usted dice el nombre. Luego, repita los nombres en orden. Después, pida a su hijo que sea el líder y recuerde los nombres y el orden de todos los muebles que usted toque.

Diviértete con el lenguaje

Léale un libro a su hijo sobre algo grande y algo pequeño. Pida a su hijo que señale cuál es el más grande y cuál es el más pequeño. A continuación encontrará algunos títulos:

The Lion and the Mouse by Aesop's Fable
Little Penguin by Patrick Benson
Where's My Teddy? by Jez Alborough

School-Home Link
Newsletter 28

Some New Words We've Learned
- library
- chain saw
- restaurant
- traffic light
- librarian
- bulldozer
- customer

Activity Update
We played a game of "Occupation Concentration" to help us learn about the tools people use in different occupations. You can help your child review this information by playing a word game. Give your child the name of a tool, and ask your child to tell you who would use that tool.

- paintbrush—painter
- cash register—checker
- thermometer—nurse or doctor
- fire engine—firefighter
- dentist's chair—dentist
- airplane—pilot
- saw—carpenter
- tractor—farmer
- traffic light—policeman or driver
- chain saw—lumberjack

More Opposites
Here are some more opposites you can help your child learn. Give your child one word. Ask your child to say the opposite.

- hot/cold
- open/close
- late/early
- sick/well
- sad/happy
- awake/asleep
- fast/slow

Things to Talk About at Home
Absurdity
Your child has been learning that something that is *absurd* is *very silly*. Give your child some examples and see if he or she can tell you whether or not they are absurd. Here are some examples:

not absurd
"I talked to Grandma on the phone today."

"I saw a rabbit in our yard."

absurd
"I talked to Santa Claus on the phone today."

"I saw an elephant in our yard."

Absurd Pictures
Have fun making some absurd pictures with your child. You will need a magazine, scissors, and glue. Cut out pictures from the magazine and change them to be silly. For example: if you find a picture of a girl talking on a phone, cut out a picture of a shoe and paste it over the phone. Ask your child to explain why the picture is absurd.

Language Fun
Share some of the Dr. Seuss books with your child. Talk about what is absurd in the stories. Dr. Seuss stories make us laugh because they are so absurd. Here are some titles.

> *The Cat in the Hat*
> *And to Think That I Saw It on Mulberry Street!*
> *If I Ran the Zoo*

Ask your librarian for more Dr. Seuss books.

Conexión con la escuela y la casa
Boletín 28

Algunas palabras que hemos aprendido
- library
- librarian
- chain saw
- bulldozer
- restaurant
- customer
- traffic light

Actividades de última hora
Jugamos un juego de "Ocupación concentración" para poder aprender las herramientas que las personas usan en diferentes ocupaciones. Usted puede ayudar a su hijo a repasar esta información jugando un juego de palabras. Diga a su hijo el nombre de la herramienta y pídale que le diga quién usaría esta herramienta.

- paintbrush—painter
- cash register—checker
- thermometer—nurse or doctor
- fire engine—firefighter
- dentist's chair—dentist
- airplane—pilot
- saw—carpenter
- tractor—farmer
- traffic light—policeman or driver
- chain saw—lumberjack

Más opuestos
A continuación encontrará más palabras opuestas con las cuales puede ayudar a que su hijo aprenda. Dígale una palabra a su hijo y pídale que le diga el opuesto.

- hot/cold
- sad/happy
- open/close
- awake/asleep
- late/early
- fast/slow
- sick/well

Cosas sobre qué conversar en el hogar
Absurdo
Su hijo ha aprendido que algo que es absurdo es muy tonto. Dé a su hijo algunos ejemplos y vea si él o ella puede decirle si son absurdos o no. A continuación encontrará algunos ejemplos:

no es absurdo
"Hoy hablé por teléfono con mi abuela."

"Vi un conejo en nuestro jardín."

absurdo
"Hoy hablé por teléfono con San Nicolás."

"Vi un elefante en nuestro jardín."

Ilustraciones absurdas
Diviértase elaborando algunas ilustraciones con su hijo. Necesitará una revista, unas tijeras y pegamento. Recorte las ilustraciones de la revista y cámbielas de manera que parezcan tontas. Por ejemplo: si consigue una ilustración de una muchacha hablando por teléfono, recorte un zapato y péguelo encima del teléfono. Pida a su hijo que explique por qué la ilustración es absurda.

Diviértete con el lenguaje
Comparta con su hijo alguno de los libros del Dr. Seuss. Hable sobre qué es absurdo en las historias. Las historias del Dr. Seuss nos hacen reír porque son sumamente absurdas. A continuación encontrará algunos títulos.

The Cat in the Hat
And to Think That I Saw It on Mulberry Street!
If I Ran the Zoo

Pídale al bibliotecario más libros del Dr. Seuss.

School-Home Link
Newsletter 29

Some New Words We've Learned

Animals
- leopard
- parrot
- snake

Airport
- runway
- hangar
- airport terminal
- baggage cart

Fire Station
- engine
- siren
- fire pole
- fire extinguisher
- emergency light

Activity Update

Your child made a book about jungle animals. Ask your child to tell you the names of the animals in the book. Then have your child show you how to make absurd animals. Ask your child to tell you why the animals are absurd.

Make a Jungle Snake

Snakes live in the jungle and like to crawl on the ground and up trees. Your child can make a snake to hang in your house. You will need a paper plate, pencil, crayons, scissors, and string. Here's what to do:

1. Poke a hole in the center of the paper plate.
2. Start at the hole and draw a spiral out to the edge of the plate.
3. Color the plate on both sides using bright "snake" colors.
4. Start at the edge of the plate and cut along the spiral line to the center.
5. Tie a string through the center hole. Hang the snake up and watch it move in the air!

Things to Talk About at Home

Fire Safety

Your child has been learning about a fire station and the equipment used by firefighters. Talk with your child about fire safety in your home. Discuss what you would do in case of a fire. Remind your child never to play with matches or candles. Ask your child to repeat your address and phone number, as well as the 911 emergency number.

Airport Words

Play a game about airports with your child. Say, "I'll name things that are at the airport, but don't let me fool you. If I name something that is not found at the airport, you say, 'No.' If I name something that is at the airport, you say, 'Yes.' Here I go!"

- runway
- horse
- ship
- jungle
- couch
- helicopter
- clown
- baggage cart
- suitcase
- airport terminal
- airplane
- pilot
- river
- hangar

Language Fun

Here's a fun poem to say with your child about some little monkeys that got into the house!

Five little monkeys jumping on the bed.
One fell off and bumped his head.
Mama called the doctor, the doctor said,
"Keep those monkeys off that bed!"
Four little monkeys jumping on the bed.
(Repeat until no monkeys are left.)

Conexión con la escuela y la casa
Boletín 29

Algunas palabras que hemos aprendido

Animales
- leopard
- parrot
- snake

Aeropuerto
- runway
- hangar
- airport terminal
- baggage cart

Estación de bomberos
- engine
- siren
- fire pole
- fire extinguisher
- emergency light

Actividades de última hora

Su hijo hizo un libro sobre los animales de la selva. Pida a su hijo que le diga los nombres de los animales del libro. Luego, pida a su hijo que le muestre cómo hacer animales absurdos. Pida a su hijo que le diga por qué los animales son absurdos.

Hacer una serpiente de la selva

Las serpientes viven en la selva y les gusta arrastrarse por el suelo y trepar por los árboles. Su hijo puede hacer una serpiente para colgarla en su casa. Necesitará un plato de papel, un lápiz, creyones, tijeras y un resorte. Esto es lo que hay que hacer:

1. Haga un hueco en el centro del plato de papel.

2. Dibuje una espiral comenzando desde el hueco hasta la orilla del plato.

3. Coloree el plato por ambos lados usando colores brillantes como de "serpiente."

4. Recorte la línea de la espiral comenzando desde la orilla del plato hasta el centro.

5. Amarre un resorte a través del hueco del centro. ¡Cuelgue la serpiente y obsérvela como se mueve en el aire!

Cosas sobre qué conversar en el hogar
Seguridad contra incendios

Su hijo ha aprendido sobre las estaciones de bomberos y el equipo usado por los bomberos. Hable con su hijo sobre la seguridad contra incendios en el hogar. Comente qué haría en caso de un incendio. Recuérdele a su hijo nunca jugar con fósforos o con velas. Pida a su hijo que repita su dirección y su número telefónico, así como el número de emergencia 911.

Palabras del aeropuerto

Juegue con su hijo un juego sobre los aeropuertos. Diga: "Nombraré cosas que se encuentran en el aeropuerto, pero no dejes que te engañe. Si nombro algo que no se encuentra en el aeropuerto, dices 'No.' Si nombro algo que se encuentra en el aeropuerto dices 'Sí.' ¡Aquí vamos!"

- pista de aterrizaje
- caballo
- barco
- selva
- sofá
- helicóptero
- payaso
- carro de equipaje
- maleta
- terminal del aeropuerto
- avión
- piloto
- río
- hangar

Diviértete con el lenguaje

A continuación encontrará un gracioso poema para que se lo cuente a su hijo sobre unos ¡monitos que entraron a la casa!

Five little monkeys jumping on the bed.
One fell off and bumped his head.
Mama called the doctor, the doctor said,
"Keep those monkeys off that bed!"
Four little monkeys jumping on the bed.
(Repeat until no monkeys are left.)

School-Home Link
Newsletter 30

Some New Words We've Learned

Garage
- mechanic
- jack
- tools
- garage
- air hose

Restaurant
- menu
- cashier
- cook

Library
- bookshelves
- computer

Activity Update

We made a menu to help us practice ordering a meal in a restaurant. Ask your child to show you the menu and tell you what foods are on it.

Order Up!

You can make some play clay for your child to create "food." Then you can pretend to be a customer in a restaurant. Your child can be the waiter or waitress. Order your meal off the menu and your child can bring the pretend food to you.

Here's how to make the clay.

Mix:

2 cups of flour
1 cup of salt
1 cup of water (add more if needed)

Divide the clay into several batches. Add a few drops of food coloring to each batch.

Things to Talk About at Home

Restaurant Manners

Talk to your child about eating in a restaurant. Remind your child that other people are eating there, too. Using good manners helps everyone enjoy eating out. When you don't run, talk softly, eat neatly, use your napkin, and sit quietly, it shows that you have good restaurant manners.

Who Am I? Pantomime

Here is an occupations game you can play with your child.

1. Discuss the jobs done by a cashier, mechanic, librarian, lumberjack, police officer, and farmer.

2. Ask your child to act out one of these occupations for you to guess.

3. Take turns acting out different occupations.

Language Fun

Here is a song you and your child can sing about a firefighter. Sing it to the tune of "I'm a Little Teapot."

I'm a firefighter dressed in red,
With my helmet on my head.
I can drive the engine, fight fire, too.
And help make things safe for you!

Conexión con la escuela y la casa
Boletín 30

Algunas palabras que hemos aprendido

Taller mecánico
- mechanic
- jack
- tools
- garage
- air hose

Restaurante
- menu
- cashier
- cook

Biblioteca
- bookshelves
- computer

Actividades de última hora

Elaboramos un menú para practicar cómo ordenar una comida en un restaurante. Pida a su hijo que le muestre el menú y que le diga cuál es la comida que hay.

¡Ordenar!

Usted puede elaborar para su hijo algunos "alimentos" con arcilla para jugar. Luego, puede pretender ser un cliente de un restaurante. Su hijo puede ser el mesonero o la mesonera. Ordene su comida del menú y su hijo puede pretender traerle el alimento.

A continuación encontrará cómo hacer la arcilla.

Mezcle:

2 tazas de harina
1 taza de sal
1 taza de agua (agregar más si se necesita)

Separe la arcilla en varios lotes. Agregue unas gotas de colorante en cada uno de los lotes.

Cosas sobre qué conversar en el hogar

Modales en un restaurante

Hable con su hijo acerca de comer en un restaurante. Recuérdele que allí también comen otras personas. Usar buenos modales ayuda a que todos se diviertan al salir a comer. Cuando no corres, hablas suave, comes con esmero, usas tu servilleta y te sientas tranquilamente, eso demuestra que tienes buenos modales.

¿Quién soy? Pantomima

A continuación encontrará algunos juegos de ocupación que puede jugar con su hijo.

1. Comente los trabajos realizados por un cajero, una bibliotecaria, un maderero, un oficial de policía y un granjero.

2. Pida a su hijo que le represente una de estas ocupaciones para que usted adivine.

3. Túrnense para representar diferentes ocupaciones.

Diviértete con el lenguaje

A continuación encontrará una canción sobre un bombero que usted y su hijo pueden cantar. Cántela con la melodía de "I'm a Little Teapot."

I'm a firefighter dressed in red,
With my helmet on my head.
I can drive the engine, fight fire, too.
And help make things safe for you!